Snapshot Pre-Interme Language Booster

Welcome to the **Language Booster**!

This book will give you lots of extra practice, not just in grammar but also in vocabulary and communication skills.

The Workbook

The Language Booster starts off with a **Workbook** section (pages 4 to 83). It's a workbook with a difference – the exercises are separated into three levels: *Stay cool* (easier exercises), *Move on* (harder exercises) and *Go for it* (challenging exercises). You and your teacher can choose the level that suits you best, or you can work through *all* the exercises if you like! When you feel confident with one level, you can move on to the next level.

As an extra bonus after every two units, there's an exciting serial story for you to read. It's called *COOL FM*, it's set in Australia, and it's about a young musician who leaves home to go to Sydney in search of fame, fortune and his girlfriend.

The Grammar Builder

Do you still need more grammar practice? The second part of the Language Booster, called the **Grammar Builder** (pages 84 to 144), contains an extra bank of grammar practice exercises and includes grammar reference sections called *Grammar highlights*, so that you can check on grammar rules when you are doing the exercises. You can work through the units in the Grammar Builder alongside the units in the Workbook section, or you can do them at a later stage for revision.

We hope that this Language Booster, with its special features, will give you all the help you need to learn English successfully – and enjoyably!

Workbook section: Chris Barker, Brian Abbs, Ingrid Freebairn
Grammar Builder section: Olivia Johnston

Contents

1 I'm here to work.

Vocabulary

Stay cool/Move on

1 Make nouns from the verbs by adding *-er*, *-r* or *-or* and write them in the correct list.

• act • dive • conduct • walk • paint
• sail • sing • swim • drive • write
• surf • drum • report

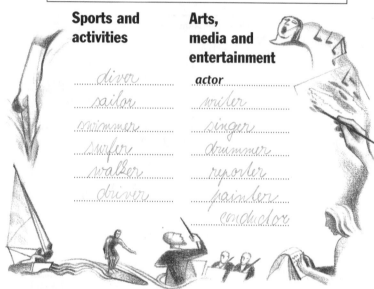

Sports and activities	Arts, media and entertainment
diver	*actor*
sailor	writer
swimmer	singer
surfer	drummer
walker	reporter
driver	painter
	conductor

Go for it

2 Complete the crossword.

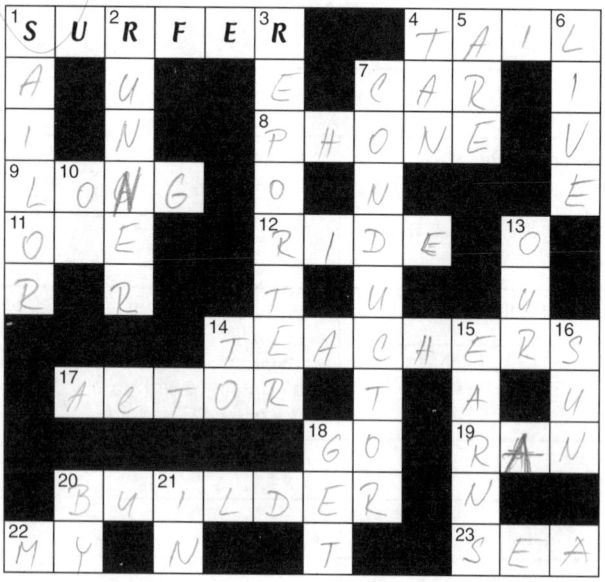

Across

1 I'm a professional ... , so I travel everywhere with my surfboard. (6)
4 'How ... are you?' 'I'm about 1.8 metres.' (4)
7 She can drive but she hasn't got a ... . (3)
8 Can I borrow your mobile ... , please? (5)
9 How ... are you in London for? (4)
11 'How often do the buses come?' 'There's ... every hour.' (3)
12 'Can he ... a horse?' 'Yes. He's a good rider.' (4)
14 There are six English ... at our school, and two of them also teach German. (8)
17 I'm studying at drama school because I want to be an ... . (5)
18 Does this bus ... to Fistral Beach? (2)
19 I was so late, I ... all the way to school! (3)
20 I build houses. I'm a ... . (7)
22 I usually come here with ... parents. (2)
23 He likes Newquay because he likes being near the ... . (3)

Down

1 I haven't got a boat but I'm a good ... . (6)
2 I do the London Marathon every year but I'm not a professional ... . (6)
3 I work for a newspaper as a ... . (8)
4 When you sit in the sun you get a ... . (3)
5 'I'm a surfer.' ' ... you?' (3)
6 You need a ... -saving certificate to be a lifeguard. (4)
7 He's the ... of a famous orchestra. (9)
10 Are you here ... holiday? (2)
13 We're here with ... parents. (3)
14 I'm here ... work. (2)
15 Gianni ... £200 a week. (5)
16 The weather's great. The ... shines every day. (3)
18 'Let's walk.' 'No, I'm tired. Let's ... the bus.' (3)
20 My name's Jake, ... the way. (2)
21 Cape Town is ... South Africa. (2)

Grammar

Stay cool

Present simple and continuous

3 > Complete the postcard using the present simple or the present continuous tense of the verbs in the box.

• stay • come • write • live • not live
• wait • work • be • like

Hi, everyone!

News from Newquay! Everyone _is waiting_ for the surfing championships to begin. They _are_ a very popular event and thousands of people ¹...._come_.... to Cornwall every summer to watch them.

I've already got some good friends here. One is an Italian guy called Gianni. He's a lifeguard on the beach and he ²...._staying_.... at the same guesthouse as I am. Then there's a girl called Nicola. She's here for the summer holidays. She ³...._working_.... for her aunt, who has a hotel here. The rest of the year, she ⁴...._doesn't_.... in Newquay; she ⁵...._lives_.... in London with her parents. I ⁶...._like_.... her very much.

I ⁷...._writing_.... this postcard at a café on the beach. Life's hard!

See you soon,
    Alan

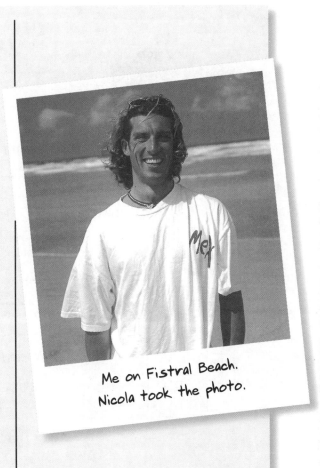

Me on Fistral Beach.
Nicola took the photo.

Infinitive of purpose

4 > Match an action in the left-hand column with a purpose in the right-hand column to make complete sentences.

1 I'm going to the bathroom
2 They're staying at home tonight
3 I'm washing cars at a garage
4 I want to buy a new shirt
5 She listens to British pop songs
6 I'm writing to my aunt
7 John wants to go to college
8 I'm going to the shopping mall

a) to wear at Mel's party.
b) to thank her for my present.
c) to study Art.
d) to improve her English.
e) to buy some new trainers.
f) to earn some extra money.
g) to watch football on TV.
h) to change the towels.

○○ Move on/Go for it

Present simple and continuous

5 ⟩ Use the pictures and prompts to write questions and answers in the present simple or continuous.

What / Sasha / Anna / do?
What are Sasha and Anna doing?
They're playing tennis.

1 How / Martin / usually / get to / school?
How usually Martin get to school
He usually get to school by bike.

2 Karen / work / restaurant / this summer?
Is Karen working in a restaurant?
this summer? No, she is not working in restaurant
this summer. She is working in Boutique

3 What / they / often / do / on Friday evenings?
What do they often do on F. evenings?
They go to the cinema.

4 Where / Kyoko / study / this year?
Where is Kyoko studying this year?
She is studying at London college of fashion

Infinitive of purpose

6 ⟩ Join the sentences using the infinitive of the verbs in the box to describe these people's plans.

- study
- visit
- learn
- earn
- raise

Carol wants to speak Spanish. She's going to Madrid for three months.

Carol's going to Madrid for three months to learn Spanish.

1 Bob's working in a supermarket. He needs some extra money.
Bob's working in a supermarket to earn some extra money.

2 We need money for our school. We're doing a sponsored swim.
We need money for our school to raise a sponsored swim.

3 Shari's going to college. She's got a place on the Law course.
Shari's going to college to study on the Law course.

4 My grandmother's ill. I'm going to the hospital.
My grandmother's ill. I'm going to visit her to the hospital.

Communication

○ Stay cool

7 > Write the echo questions in the correct place in the conversation.

| • Are you? | • Do you? | • Does it? |
| • (Have you?) | • Is it? | |

A: I've got a part-time job.

B: *Have you?*

A: Yes, but it's just for the summer season.

B: ¹ *Is it?*

A: Yes, because I'm going to college in the autumn.

B: ² *Are you?* Do you like the job?

A: It's OK but I have to work shifts.

B: ³ *Does it.* ~~To you?~~

A: I must go now. The late shift starts at 6 p.m.

B: ⁴ *Are you?* ~~Does it?~~

A: Yes, and I don't want to be late! Bye!

○○ Move on

8 > Complete the conversations.

  A: Do you live near here?
  B: Yes, I _live_ in the next street.
  A: _Do you?_ I live miles away.

1 **A:** Do you listen to music when you're studying?
  B: Yes, _~~I am~~_ (I do)
  I _'m listening_ a CD player in my room.
  A: _Are you (do you)_? I've only got a radio.

2 **A:** I went to the new pizzeria last night.
  B: _did you_ ?
  A: Yes, it _is_ really good.
  B: _Is it_ ?
  A: We can go on Friday evening, if you like.
  B: _Can you_ ? Brilliant!

3 **A:** I've just seen Claire. She was going into town with Andy.
  B: _Was she_ ?
  A: Yes. And they were holding hands.
  B: _Were they_ ? Maybe she and Peter have split up.
  A: Maybe.

○○○ Go for it

9 > In your notebook, continue the conversation between Kate and Jay. Kate asks:

- where the courts are.
- what time the courts open.
- how much it costs to play.
- about taking lessons.
- about playing tennis with Jay.

West Hill Park
TENNIS COURTS
Lawn Road

Open from 10.00 a.m.
Courts: £6.50 per hour
Lessons: £20 per hour

Kate: *Excuse me, can you tell me where the tennis courts are?*

Jay: *Yes, of course. They're on Lawn Road. I'm going there now.*

Kate: *Are you? .....?*

? What's wrong?

10 > Circle the mistakes in these sentences using the key. Then correct them.

Key	
p = punctuation	**w.o.** = word order
gr = grammar	**sp** = spelling
^ = there is a word missing	**v** = vocabulary

'We're saving (money go) on holiday.'

_^_ *We're saving money to go on holiday.*

1 They're looking for a drumer for the band.
  _sp_ ....

2 We go there usually in July.
  _w.o._ ....

3 They're going to the same place every year.
  _gr_ ....

4 I dont like it when the weather's bad.
  _p_ ....

5 Nicola's got a half-time job as a waitress.
  _v_ ....

2 > Over three hours late.

Vocabulary

○ **Stay cool/Move on**

1 > Circle nine more types of transport in this wordsquare.

B	I	T	R	A	M
K	B	R	U	S	F
C	O	A	C	H	E
A	A	I	L	I	R
R	T	N	R	P	R
P	L	A	N	E	Y
O	B	U	S	W	L
S	B	I	K	E	L

2 > Write in the missing words. Then number the phrases in sequence from distant past to recent past.

> • last   • yesterday   • ago

a) five minutes .... ☐

b) .... month ☐

c) this afternoon ☐

d) this morning ☐

e) three months .... ☐

f) two days .... ☐

g) .... afternoon ☐

h) .... week ☐

i) ...***last***... year **1**

j) .... night ☐

k) .... morning ☐

○○○ **Go for it**

3 > Complete these newspaper extracts with the correct past time adverbials and prepositions.

A The competition started ...***yesterday***... morning ¹......... nine o'clock and finished just after eight o'clock ²............ the evening. After the opening

B ☆☆☆☆☆☆☆☆☆☆☆☆

The band are now touring Ireland but ³.............. weekend, they gave a concert at Alexandra Palace here in London. They played their first song at eight thirty and left the stage ⁴.............. midnight. A year ⁵.............. , they were unknown. Now they are one of Britain's

C The US President arrived ⁶............... night and met the Prime Minister ⁷............... morning for talks about

D The wedding took place ⁸.............. Friday 5 June. The couple, who only met three months ⁹.............. , are spending their honeymoon in

Grammar

○ Stay cool

Past simple
Linkers

4 > Use the prompts and the linkers to explain what happened at the disco.

trip / over his coat
1 knock / over a drink
2 step / on a girl's toes
3 climb / onto a table to dance
4 fall / off the table and break / his arm

> • After that • Then • In the end
> • First • And then

'Did Martin enjoy the disco?'
'No, it was awful.'
'Why, what happened?'

'**First, he tripped over his coat.**

1 *After that he stepped on a girl's toes,*
2 *And then climbed onto a table to dance*
3 *Then he knocked over a drink*

4 *In the end falled off the table and break his arm,*

Conjunctions *so* and *because*

5 > Choose *so* or *because* to join these sentences.

Nicola and Jake were at the same bus stop *so* they started talking.

1 Nicola's aunt is the manager of a hotel ....*so*............ she offered Nicola a job.
2 Nicola was tired ....*because*............ she had a bad journey.
3 The train stopped for ages ....*because*............ there was a signal failure.
4 Nicola wrote to Suzy ....*because*............ she wanted to tell her about the journey.
5 She's starting her job tomorrow ....*because*............ she's going to relax today.

○○ Move on

Past simple

6 > Complete the text by putting the verbs in brackets in the correct past tense form.

Transport Timeline	
1500	Leonardo da Vinci (design) **designed** a helicopter.
1620	Cornelius van Drebbel (build) 1 *build* a submarine.
1783	Pilatre de Rozier and the Marquis d'Arlandes (make) 2 *made* the first flight in a hot-air balloon.
1791	Comte Mede de Sivrac (design) 3 *designed* a bicycle without pedals.
1829	George Shillibeer (introduce) 4 *introduced* horse-drawn buses to London.
1829	George Stephenson's locomotive *The Rocket* (win) 5 *won* a competition.
1837	Steam trams (begin) 6 *began* to operate in New York City.
1843	The *Great Britain* steamship (sail) 7 *sailed* across the Atlantic Ocean.
1863	The first underground railway (open) 8 *opened* in London.
1885	Karl Benz and Gottlieb Daimler (invent) 9 *invented* the petrol engine.
1909	Louis Blériot (fly) 10 *flew* from France to England in a monoplane.

Go for it

Past simple
Conjunctions *so* and *because*

7 > Complete the captions using *so* or *because* and the past simple tense.

There was nothing on TV *__so we played__* cards.

1 We ran to school ....*because*....
....*we missed*.... the bus.

2 Simon was ill at the weekend ....*so we*....
....*didn't play*.... football.

3 It was Tanya's birthday last week ....*so*....
....*we made*.... a cake.

4 They didn't do their homework ....*because*....
....*they went*.... a football match.

5 Why did Amy go to the pet shop? ....*Because*....
....*she went to buy*.... some goldfish.

10

Past simple
Linkers

8 > Last year John West travelled to Finland on a school trip. In your notebook, write about his trip using his diary and the words below.

> TRIP TO FINLAND
>
> Sat.
> Arrival: Oulu, in the north of Finland
> Very cold: minus 25°C
> Accommodation: a small village
>
> Sun.
> Day with a reindeer herdsman and his reindeer
> Evening: Begin video project – 'Life in a Lapland village'
>
> Mon.
> Morning: A chance to drive snowmobiles! Great fun!
> Afternoon: Preparation of the script for our video
> Pictures for project – postcards in local shop!
>
> Tue./Wed.
> Video – 'Life in a Lapland village'
>
> Thu.
> Souvenirs from local shop
> Party
>
> Fri.
> Departure: plane at 11.30 a.m.

Verbs

- begin • (arrive) • have • drive
- be • find • spend • leave • make
- prepare • buy • stay

Linkers

- first • then • before/after that
- later • the next day

On Saturday, they arrived in Oulu in the north of Finland. ...

Communication

Stay cool

9 Complete the dialogue.

A: *Where did you go* last weekend?

B: I went to York to see a friend at the university.

A: Did you? [1] ..... *How did you go* ..... ?

B: By coach.

A: Really? [2] ..... *How long did it take* ..... ?

B: Four hours.

A: [3] ..... *Was the journey OK* ..... ?

B: It wasn't too bad.

A: [4] ..... *What did you do* ..... in York?

B: We just walked around during the day and went to the theatre in the evening.

Move on/Go for it

10 In your notebook, write a dialogue between you and an English friend from London using the prompts and the pictures.

Ask about his/her holiday destination.

You: *Where did you go for your holidays?*

Friend: *I went to Ibiza.*

1 Ask about means of transport.

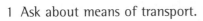

How did you go? travel
By airplane.
and by boat.

2 Ask how long the journey took.

How long did it take?
15 hours

3 Express surprise and ask what happened.

late   missed

What happened!

4 Ask what he/she did in Ibiza.

What did you do in Ibiza
He surfed and tanned

What's wrong?

11 Circle and correct the mistakes.

He got (on) the car and drove away.
He got in the car and drove away.

1 'When was your birthday?' 'Two weeks (before.)'
..... *ago* .....

2 I came (with) (the) train.
..... *by* .....

3 She (didnt) go to work yesterday.
..... *didn't* .....

4 We (bought) new computer last week.
..... *a   buy* .....

5 I saw her yesterday (evning.)
..... *evening* .....

6 How long it (took?)
..... *take?   grammar* .....

Culture snapshot

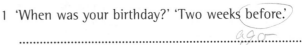

Who travels by train the most?

	km per year per person
Japan	3,223
Switzerland	1,914
Austria	1,207
France	1,013
The Netherlands	991
Denmark	890
Italy	850
Hungary	819
Germany	714
Sweden	683
Belgium	666
Finland	593
Portugal	577
Norway	537
Britain	524
Spain	419
Ireland	303
Greece	167
USA	81

Do these figures surprise you? How would you explain the differences between countries?

COOL FM

1 Trouble at home

February 25th was just another sunny day in Gosford, a small Australian town on the Central Coast north of Sydney. Scott Patterson was sitting on the front step of his house, looking at a photo and reading a letter.

> Friday January 24th
>
> Dear Scott,
>
> Guess what! My dad's got a new job as a reporter for the Sydney Morning Herald so we're moving to Sydney next week. I'm really excited to be leaving sleepy old Gosford at last and I'm looking forward to meeting new people.
> I think maybe you should try to meet new people, too. We've known each other for a long time. Perhaps we're getting boring.
>
> When I get to Sydney, I'll write and send you my new address.
>
> Love,
>
> Natalie

Scott's sister Megan came out of the house.

'Are you still looking at Natalie's photo and reading that letter?' she said. 'She left over a month ago, you know. Maybe she found a good-looking surfer on Bondi Beach.' Megan liked to tease Scott.

'Maybe.'

'Well, if you're missing her so much, why don't you do something about it? Get on a train and go and see her.'

'Without an address? Yeah, yeah.'

'Anyway, I'm going out. See you later.'

Scott went to his room to play his guitar. A few minutes later, his mother knocked at the door.

'What are you doing, Scott?'

'I'm writing a song.'

His mother came into the room.

'For goodness' sake, Scott, you can't spend all summer just playing your guitar. You must fill in your college application form. I'm sure a lot of students are applying for Accountancy courses.'

'Oh, yeah, sure. Everybody wants to become a boring accountant.'

'Like me, you mean.'

'No, Mum. I didn't mean that. Sorry.'

That night, Scott went to bed early, but he couldn't sleep. He kept thinking about Natalie, and his music, and the Accountancy course. Eventually, at half past five in the morning, Scott put a few things in his rucksack and picked up his guitar. He wrote a note to his mother. 'Mum, Sorry about last night. I'm going away for a few days to find a job. I'll phone you when I get something. Love, Scott.'

Half an hour later, he was on the train to Sydney.

In your notebook, answer the questions.

1 What does Natalie's letter tell Scott?
2 Why can't Scott go and see Natalie?
3 What does Scott's mother want him to do?
4 What is Scott interested in?
5 Where is Scott going?

3 A place which attracts tourists.

Vocabulary

○ Stay cool

1 Match the words with the pictures.

1 sea   **a**

2 forest   ☑

3 rock   ☑

4 valley   ☐

5 field   ☐

6 mountain   ☐

7 river   ☐

8 bay   ☐

9 lake   ☐

10 cave   ☐

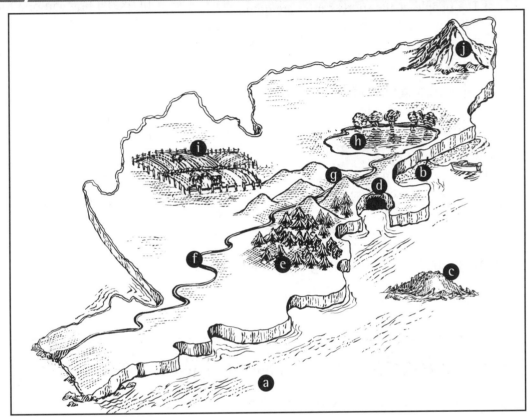

○○ Move on

prep

2 Complete the words.

The Hebrides

The **islands** which lie off the west
[1] c o a s t of Scotland are called the
Inner and Outer Hebrides. As you
approach them by boat, you notice
the spectacular [2] c o a s t l i n e
with white sandy [3] b e a c h e s,
wide [4] b a y s and rocky [5] cov e s.

Most of the people who live in
the Hebrides work in the tourist or
fishing industries. The fish come either from the [6] s e a
or from the many [7] r i v e r s and [8] l a k e s
which are a feature of all the islands. Farming is also
important to the economy of the islands. The farmers
keep their sheep in [9] f o r e s t near their farms
or on the open [10] m o o r s.

The wildlife of the islands is rich and
varied and a great attraction for visitors.
Seals swim in and out of [11] c a v e s or
lie on [12] r o c ks in the sun. Millions of sea
birds live on the rocky [13] c l i f f s of
many of the small, uninhabited islands. The
golden eagle, which is now protected, is
starting to return to its home in the isolated
[14] m o u n t a i n s and
[15] v a l l e y s of the islands.

○○○ Go for it

3 In your notebook, write a description of a
region in your country. Use some of the words
from Exercises 1 and 2.

Grammar

Stay cool

Future with *going to, will* or present continuous

4 > Circle the correct response.

I'd like to join a yoga class.
a) The people at the sports centre are going to tell you about the classes.
b) The people at the sports centre will tell you about the classes.

1 Do you want to go to the cinema this evening?
a) Sorry, we're going to Anna's house.
b) Sorry, we'll go to Anna's house.

2 I hate that new CD.
a) OK, OK. We won't play it again.
b) OK, OK. We aren't playing it again.

3 I'd really like a mobile phone.
a) OK, I'm buying you one for your birthday.
b) OK, I'll buy you one for your birthday.

4 You know we've got a test on Monday.
a) Yes. I'm afraid I'm not going to pass it.
b) Yes. I'm afraid I'm not passing it.

5 There are no lessons on Friday!
a) I know. We'll go on a school trip.
b) I know. We're going on a school trip.

6 What's your New Year's Resolution?
a) I'm going to save money next year.
b) I'm saving money next year.

Defining and non-defining relative clauses

5 > Complete the sentences with *who, which* **or** *where.*

Students Why is homework sometimes a problem?

You've got a little brother **who'** s great but [1] *who* makes a lot of noise.

Your older sister, [2] *who* is at college, needs the computer to do her work.

You've got a room [3] *which* is too small.

What's the answer?

The Computer and Homework Club

- Students [4] *who* have problems doing homework at home can come here and work.
- We have a large room [5] *where* students can do homework and a computer room with programs [6] *which* are specifically designed to help with school work.
- We also have some programs [7] *which* are purely for fun.
- There will always be somebody [8] *who* will help you.
- The club, [9] *which* is close to Ladbroke Grove, is open from 3.30 to 6.00 p.m.

Anything else?

- Our computer courses, [10] *which* are free for students under 16, take place on Monday and Wednesday evenings.
- And we have a coffee bar [11] *where* you can meet other students.

⊙⊙ Move on

Future with *going to, will* or present continuous

6 > **Complete the dialogues with the verbs in the box. Use the present continuous,** *(not) going to* **or** *will/won't.*

> • be   • meet   • cook   (• answer)
> • bring   • have   • buy

A: The phone's ringing.
B: Leave it! I'm **not going to answer** it.

1 **A:** Where's your homework, Gary?
  B: I'm sorry. I *'ll bringing I'll buying / will bring* it to class tomorrow.

2 **A:** We need to be at the station at six o'clock.
  B: OK. I*'ll meeting* you at your house at five thirty.

3 **A:** Have you decided on a present for Julie?
  B: Yes. I *~~'ll~~ buy* (*going to*) her a speedometer for her bike.

4 **A:** Bye! I'll see you at Rosa's house on Saturday.
  B: Oh, I forgot. She *is ~~standing~~ having* a party, isn't she?

5 **A:** I don't like fish, Sam doesn't eat meat and Adam doesn't like vegetables.
  B: Well, hard luck! I *'m cooking* three different dishes!

6 **A:** Let's go and see if Leo's at home.
  B: No, he *won't be* there. He's on holiday.

⊙⊙⊙ Go for it

Future with *going to, will* or present continuous
Defining and non-defining relative clauses

7 > **Use the prompts with** *'ll (will), going to* **or the present continuous to complete the first part of the conversation.**

Simon: Oh, no!
Jack: What's the problem?
Simon: (Kate / come round) **Kate's coming round** in half an hour. I'm making her a surprise cake for her birthday, but (it / not be) 1 *it won't be* ready.
Jack: Phone and tell her to come round tomorrow.

Simon: (She / go) 2 *is going* to her grandparents' tomorrow.
Jack: Well, go out and buy a cake.
Simon: No, no, (I / not buy) 3 *I won't buy* one.
Jack: Why don't you take her to the cinema for her birthday instead? (She / like) 4 *She will like* that.
Simon: That's a good idea. (I / phone) 5 *I'll phone* the Trocadero to see what's on.
Jack: OK. What (you / do) 6 *will you do* with the cake mixture?
Simon: I think (I / put) 7 *I'll put it* it in the fridge.

Now complete the second part of the conversation with the relative pronouns *who, which* **or** *where.*

Jack: The Trocadero is the cinema **where** I went with Yvonne on our first date. It's the one 8 *which* has got an enormous screen and fantastic sound.
Simon: Excellent.
Jack: And there's a place next door 9 *where* they serve brilliant pizzas.
Simon: Even better.
Jack: And I know someone 10 *who* works there as a waiter. I think you're going to have a great evening!

Communication

○ Stay cool

8 > Fill in the missing words. Then rewrite the conversation in the correct order.

A ③ What are you ......*doing*...... on Saturday evening?

B ⑥ Yes. That ......*will*...... be great.

B ② Yes, I'm quite busy. I'm ......*going*...... out on Tuesday and I think I'm ......*going*...... in a volleyball match on Thursday.

A ⑤ Because I've got two tickets for the *Aqua* concert at the Apollo on Saturday. Do you ......*fancy*...... coming?

A ① ..*Are*.. you busy next week?

B ④ Saturday? I'm not sure. Why?

A: *Are you busy next week?*

B: ....

A: ....

B: ....

A: ....

B: ....

○○ Move on

9 > Write a similar conversation using the prompts.

A: you / do / Saturday?

  What are you doing on Saturday?

B: visit / Gran / in hospital / afternoon

  1 *I'm visiting Gran in hospital afternoon*

A: free / Saturday morning?

  2 *Are you free Saturday morning.*

B: ✓

  3 *Yes, I'm*

A: Laser Exhibition / you / fancy / come?

  4 *Do you fancy coming L.E*

B: ✓

  5 *Yes, I do.*

A: phone / Friday evening / arrange a time

  6 *I'll phone you arrange a time on Friday evening*

○○○ Go for it

10 > Invite a friend to go on a camping trip. He/She can't go this weekend but next weekend is possible. Write the conversation in your notebook.

You: *Are you busy this weekend?*
Friend: *Yes, ...*

STUDY CORNER

Noting context
When you learn a new expression, note down the context in which it is used and the translation.

11 > In your notebook, write the context and the translation of these expressions, which include *will*.

Expression	Context	Translation
I'll go.	*When the doorbell or the phone rings*	
I'll see you later.		
I'll have a coffee.		
I'll do it for you.		
I'll think about it.		
I'll take the blue one, please.		

How long have you been here?

Vocabulary

◯ Stay cool/Move on

1 Complete the captions by using the adjectives in their positive and negative forms.

- comfortable
- expensive
- (healthy)
- interesting
- pleasant
- popular

a healthy
breakfast

an unhealthy
breakfast

1 *interesting*
book

uninteresting
book

2 *a comfortable*
chair

an uncomfortable
chair

3 *a pleasant*
smell

an unpleasant
smell

4 *an expensive*
bike

a cheap
bike

5 *a popular*
player

an unpopular
player

◯◯◯ Go for it

the most depended

2 Complete the list of opposites.

Adjective	Opposite
healthy	**unhealthy**
dirty	**clean**
hot	*the last hot* cold
fast	slow
good	bad
cheap	expensive
wet	dry
beautiful	*un*
usual	unusual
dependent	independent
successful	unsuccessful
formal	informal
practical	impractical
correct	incorrect
fashionable	unfashionable
important	unimportant
possible	impossible
mature	immature

Grammar

Stay cool

Present perfect simple with *for* and *since*

3 Write sentences using the present perfect with *for* or *since*.

He / be in Madrid / September

He's been in Madrid since September.

1 I / have a headache / two days

I have had a headache for two days

2 she / be on the phone / two hours?

Has she been on the phone for two hours?

3 They / live in Paris / ages

They have live in Paris for ages.

4 We / not have any letters / a week

We haven't had any letters for a week.

5 She / do a lot of work / Tuesday

She has done a lot of work since Tuesday

6 He / not go on holiday / three years

Have you read all those books for beginning of term.

7 you / read all those books / the beginning of term?

Have you read all those books
He hasn't gone on holiday for three years

8 I / not see my cousins / last August

I haven't seen my cousins since last August.

Comparison of adjectives

4 Use the adjectives to make comparisons.

Travelling by coach isn't **as comfortable as** (comfortable) travelling by train.
Travelling by train is **faster** (fast) than travelling by coach.
Travelling by plane is **the fastest** (fast) of all.

1 He isn't *as tall as* (tall) his sister.
2 He's *more short* (short) than his sister.
3 She's *the tallest* (tall) student in the school.

4 His second album wasn't *as good as* (good) his first album.
5 His third album was *worse* (bad) than his second album.
6 His most recent album was *the worst* (bad) album he's made.

7 Rollerblading isn't *as expensive as* (expensive) skiing.
8 Snowboarding is *much more exciting* (exciting) than rollerblading.
9 Swimming is *the most cheap* (cheap) sport of all.

In which three sentences can you use *much*?

....

18

Move on/Go for it

Present perfect simple with *for* and *since*

5 Rewrite each sentence in two ways, using *for* and *since*.

We last went to London in June.
(not go / London)

We haven't been to London since June.

We haven't been to London for six months.

2 The Close,
Newquay

3 March 1999

1 They moved to Newquay in 1990.
(live / there)

They have been lived in N. since 1990

They —11— for 9 years

Comparison of adjectives

6 Use the chart and the prompts to complete the sentences about the portable CD players.

Model	AR 1	AR 2	AR 3
Price	£149	£199	£239
Size	17 cm x 17 cm	16 cm x 16 cm	15 cm x 15 cm
Weight	250 gm	200 gm	180 gm
Sound quality	✓	✓✓	✓✓✓

(price) The AR 1 isn't **as expensive as** the AR 2.

1 (size) The AR 2 is ...bigest than... the AR 3.

2 (size) The AR 1 isn't ...as small as... the AR 3.

3 (weight) The AR 2 is ...lighter than... the AR 1.

4 (weight) The AR 3 isn't ...as havier as... the AR 1 or the AR 2.

2 He last had a letter from her in March.
(not have / a letter)

He hasn't had a letter since March for 3 months

3 I arrived at 1.30.
(be / here)

I has been here since 1.30.

I has been her for 3 hour

QUEEN'S PARK TENNIS CLUB
July 15 1999
Entrance B. Stand 2.
WD 12234-89

4 She last played tennis on July 1st.
(not play / tennis)

She hasn't played tennis since July 1x for 14 days

5 (sound quality) The AR 1 sound quality isn't ...as good as... the AR 2 sound quality.

6 (sound quality) The AR 3 sound quality is ...the best... of all.

7 In your notebook, write about yourself and your family. Use these words to help you.

- tidy
- friendly
- confident
- independent
- clever
- practical
- funny
- sporty
- mature

I've got a sister and a brother.

I'm not as tidy as ...

19

Communication

○ Stay cool/Move on

8 > Read the article. Then complete the interview using the prompts.

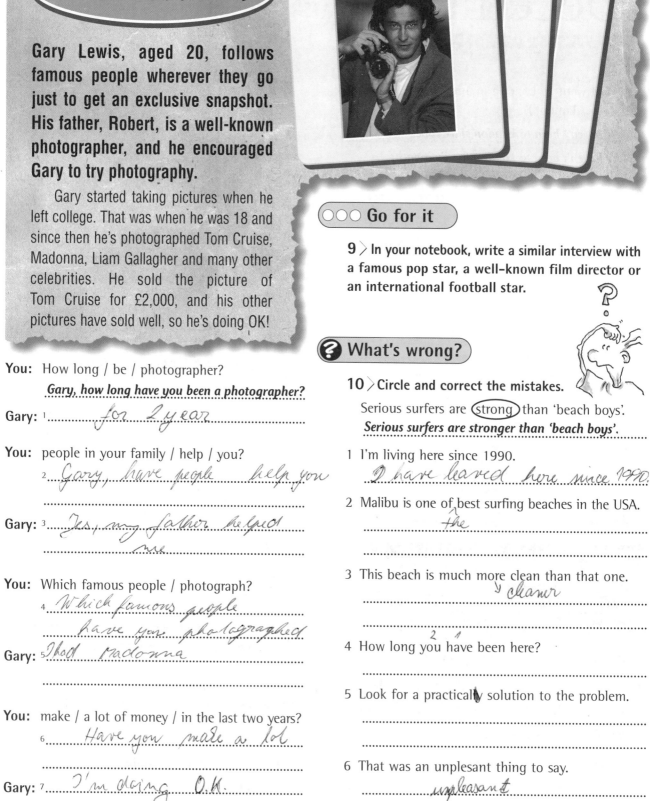

Snap-happy Gary

Gary Lewis, aged 20, follows famous people wherever they go just to get an exclusive snapshot. His father, Robert, is a well-known photographer, and he encouraged Gary to try photography.

Gary started taking pictures when he left college. That was when he was 18 and since then he's photographed Tom Cruise, Madonna, Liam Gallagher and many other celebrities. He sold the picture of Tom Cruise for £2,000, and his other pictures have sold well, so he's doing OK!

You: How long / be / photographer?
  Gary, how long have you been a photographer?

Gary: ¹.......... *for 2 year* ....

You: people in your family / help / you?
  ²*Gary, have people help you*

Gary: ³*Yes, my father helped me*

You: Which famous people / photograph?
  ⁴*Which famous people have you photographed*

Gary: ⁵*Thad Madonna*

You: make / a lot of money / in the last two years?
  ⁶*Have you make a lot*

Gary: ⁷*I'm doing O.K.*

○○○ Go for it

9 > In your notebook, write a similar interview with a famous pop star, a well-known film director or an international football star.

❓ What's wrong?

10 > Circle and correct the mistakes.

Serious surfers are (strong) than 'beach boys'.
Serious surfers are stronger than 'beach boys'.

1 I'm living here since 1990.
  I have leaved here since 1990

2 Malibu is one of best surfing beaches in the USA.
  the

3 This beach is much more clean than that one.
  cleaner

4 How long you have been here?

5 Look for a practically solution to the problem.

6 That was an unplesant thing to say.
  unpleasant

2 What are you going to do?

Scott got off the train and looked around nervously.

'What have I done?' he said to himself. For a moment, he thought about getting the next train back to Gosford. Maybe this was all a big mistake. In front of him there was a table with a sign on it saying 'COOL FM welcomes you to Sydney.' The girl behind the table smiled at him.

'Hi! How are things?' she asked.

'Fine, thanks.'

'We're doing a radio programme about young people in Sydney. We'd like to interview you, if that's all right.'

'Yes, of course.'

'Come and meet Jeff. He's the guy who's doing the interviews.'

'And so to our next guest here on COOL FM's *Welcome to Sydney* show. Hi! I'm Jeff. What's your name?'

'Scott.'

'OK, Scott, would you like to tell the listeners a bit about yourself? Is this your first time in Sydney?'

'No, but I haven't been here for a long time.'

'So where are you from?'

'I'm from Gosford, on the Central Coast.'

'What's Gosford like? I've never been there.'

'Oh, it's OK. There are good beaches nearby where you can go surfing and stuff like that.'

'But it isn't as exciting as Sydney, right?'

'You bet!'

'So what do you like doing in your spare time, Scott?'

'I play the guitar.'

'And what are you going to do in Sydney today?'

'I haven't really thought about that.'

'OK, well have a nice time, whatever you do.'

'Thanks, Scott. That was great,' said Sophie. 'Where are you staying in Sydney?'

'I haven't really got anywhere. Do you know of any places which aren't too expensive?'

'Well, there are a couple of hostels nearby. They say the one in Williams Street is better than the one in George Street, and it's more comfortable. But the one in George Street is cheaper.'

'OK, I'll try the one in George Street.'

'See you.'

'Nice guy,' said Jeff.

'Yes. But I get the impression that there's something on his mind,' said Sophie.

In your notebook, answer the questions.

1 How does Scott feel when he arrives in Sydney?
2 Why does Sophie want to interview him?
3 Has Scott been to Sydney before?
4 Why does Scott think he'll like Sydney better than Gosford?
5 Where is Scott going when he leaves the station?

Reading

The long-distance runner

Nick Bourne has left behind a career as an international fashion model to be the first person to run the length of Africa.

Nick Bourne was born in London and went to school in Cheltenham. When he left school he became a fashion model. Good-looking and 1.93 metres tall, he was very successful. He worked in New York, Paris and London.

But two years ago, at the age of 28, he returned from a trip to New York and decided to give up modelling. He wanted to focus his body and mind on running. His plan is to run the length of Africa for charity, from Cape Town in South Africa to Alexandria in Egypt. It is a journey of 9,700 kilometres. He hopes to raise £1 million for the Born Free Foundation, which protects endangered wild animals, and Save the Children, which gives help to children in need.

Nick has already run through South Africa, Botswana and Zimbabwe. Next, he plans to run through Tanzania and Kenya, where he will climb 3,000 metres up the Rift Valley. Then he will run through Ethiopia, Sudan and Egypt.

Nick's sister Emma is part of his back-up team of six people. Today, Nick is celebrating his birthday with a chocolate cake which Emma has made. He is resting, because he is recovering from malaria. His blood pressure is still high, but he will resume his journey tomorrow morning.

On a normal day, he gets up at 3.30 a.m. and starts running at

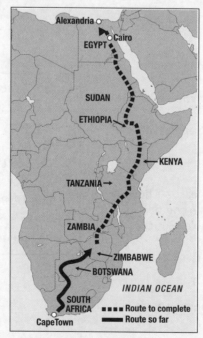

4 a.m. He does three two-hour runs a day. 'Running gives you time to think,' says Nick, 'and I love doing things people have never done before. No one's ever run across Africa.' A Norwegian professional runner, Mensen Ernst, tried to run the length of Africa in 1832. He became ill and died 500 kilometres from Cairo.

Nick's closest friend, John Adamo, says, 'They call Nick's type of running "Ultra Running". You've never seen anything like it. He runs like a wild animal.'

Since Nick began his journey, he has encountered lions, a herd of elephants and a giant cobra. 'I know there are dangers,' he says, 'but I never want to stop trying.'

He hopes to return to England in four months' time. 'I'm looking forward to cold weather again!' he says.

Comprehension

1 Write words from the text for the definitions.

a short journey .....*trip*.........

1 help, especially money, given to people who need it ..... *charity* *raise*

2 getting better after an illness ..... *recover*

3 start again ..... *resume*

4 met unexpectedly ..... *encountered*

2 Complete the information.

> **PERSONAL DETAILS**
>
> Name .....*Nick Bourne*.....
>
> Nationality ..... *English*
>
> Place of birth ..... *in London*
>
> Age *28*
>
> **JOURNEY**
>
> Length ..... *9,700 kilometres*
>
> Starting point ..... *Cape Town*
>
> Finishing point ..... *Alexandria in Egypt*
>
> Route ..... *the length of Africa*
>
> Reason for doing it *He hopes to raise £1 million for the Born Free Foundation and Save the Children*

3 Complete the interview with Nick.

What did you do before you became a runner?
I was a professional model.

1 Why are you running the length of Africa?
I'm running the for charity

2 Are there people following you to support you?
I'm recovering from malaria

3 Why are you resting at the moment?
I' run three two hour

4 How long do you run each day?
I start running at 4 am.

5 What do you miss about England?
I miss I'm looking forward to cold weather.

Communication

4 In your notebook, write an interview with Nick at the end of his run. Remember to show interest and surprise where appropriate.

Ask about:

- the reason he decided to run.
- the length of his journey.
- his back-up team.
- his worst experiences.

You: *Nick, congratulations! How do you feel?*

Nick: *I feel great. I could go on running!*

You: *Could you?* ...

Writing

5 You meet Ben Lecomte, who has just swum across the Atlantic.
In your notebook, write a newspaper report using the following details.

> **PERSONAL DETAILS**
>
> | | |
> |---|---|
> | Name | Ben Lecomte |
> | Nationality | American |
> | Place of birth | Paris, France |
> | Age | 31 |
>
> **JOURNEY**
>
> | | |
> |---|---|
> | Length | 6,000 kilometres |
> | Starting point | Cape Cod, Massachusetts |
> | Finishing point | Brittany, France |
> | Route | Across the Atlantic Ocean |
> | Reason for doing it | In memory of his father, who died in 1991. To raise £100,000 for cancer research |

Ben Lecomte was born in France, but ...

6 The car was sinking.

Vocabulary

1 Find six more verbs of movement in the wordsquare.

Y	J	T	S	D	C
P	S	W	I	M	L
B	O	U	N	C	E
F	I	M	K	M	A
A	B	J	U	M	P
L	D	I	V	E	W
L	S	R	T	Y	P

swim

1 ...jump...
2 ...dive...
3 ...bounce...
4 ...fall...
5 ...leap...
6 ...sink...

2 Use five of the verbs from Exercise 1 to complete the sentences.

Just _leap_ across. It's easy!

1 Stop! Don't .....jump..... from the side of the swimming pool! The water isn't deep enough!

2 Be careful! Don't ~~jump~~ fall .... off your bike!

3 Come on, Nigel. Let's ~~bounce~~ jump........ to the boat.

4 This is a great ball. It ~~fall~~ bounces.....really high!

3 Look at the pictures. Then in your notebook, continue the account of Sasha's circus performance.

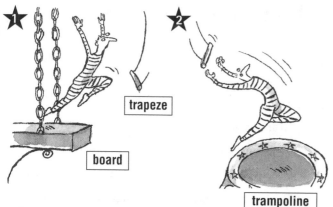

trapeze

board

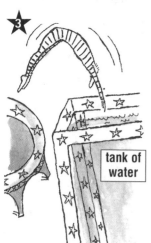

tank of water

trampoline

★ ★ Star performance ★ ★

Sasha Alexei, the star of last night's performance of The Amazing Acrobats, showed that he is only human after all!

From a board ten metres above the ground, he leapt onto the trapeze. Then he ...

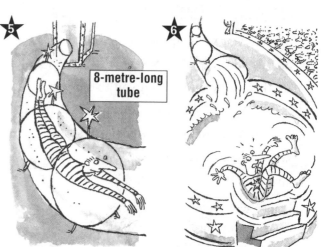

8-metre-long tube

Grammar

Past simple and continuous

4 Circle the correct phrase to complete the reply to each question about an incident in the street.

What happened?
a) A woman falls
b) (A woman fell) over in the street.
c) A woman was falling

1 When did it happen?
a) As she was coming ✓
b) As she is coming   out of the shop.
c) As she comes

2 How did she fall?
a) She was tripping
✓b) She tripped   on a paving stone.
c) She trips

3 Why did she trip?
✓a) She wasn't looking
✓b) She looked   where she was going.
c) She looks

4 Was she hurt?
a) Yes, she is hitting
✓b) Yes, she hit   her head on the ground.
c) Yes, she was hitting

5 Did you call for help?
a) Yes, we were phoning 999
b) Yes, we are phoning 999   five minutes ago.
✓c) Yes, we phoned 999

Prepositions of motion

5 Write the prepositions of motion.

i _n_ _t_ _o_   5 t _hrough_

 1 u _p_   6 t _owards_

 2 d _own_   7 a _cross_

 3 o _ver_   8 p _ast_

 4 u _nder_   9 a _long_

Past simple and continuous

6 Complete the sentences by putting one verb in the past simple and one in the past continuous.

l (try to) **was trying to** print my project when my printer (break) **broke.**

1 We (watch) ..... _were watching_ ..... TV when we (hear) ..... _heard_ ..... a strange noise. _didn't_

2 He (not go out) ..... _wasn't going out_ ..... last night because he (look after) ..... _looked_ .... _after_ ..... his young brother.

3 (you / sit) ..... _were you sitting_ ..... on the balcony when I (phone) ..... _I phoned_ ..... you?

4 I (not run) ..... _wasn't running_ ..... when I (fall) ..... _fell_ ..... over.

5 (the accident / happen) ..... _What did the accident_ .... _happen_ ..... because the bus driver (drive) ..... _drove_ ..... too fast?

6 What (she / wear) ..... _she was wearing_ ..... when you (see) ..... _saw_ ..... her?

Past simple and continuous
Time markers *when* and *while*

7 Complete the opening of this detective story using past simple or past continuous verbs in the numbered gaps and *while* or *when* in the lettered gaps.

MURDER
at Sutton Place

I (sleep) ***was sleeping*** deeply ***when*** the alarm clock [1].......*rang*........ (ring). It was only 6 a.m., so I went back to sleep.

a).....*When*..... I [2]........*woke up*........ (wake up) again, it was 9.15. I [3]........*jumped*........ (jump) quickly out of bed.

The phone rang b).....*while*..... I [4].......*was having*..... (have) a shower. I let it ring. Eventually it [5].......*stoped*........ (stop). Then it rang again c).....*when*..... I [6].....*was making*..... (make) a cup of coffee. d).....*When*..... I answered it, a woman's voice said, 'You've got to help me. Come to 12, Sutton Place as soon as you can. I'll pay anything.'

I jumped into the car. e).....*When*..... I [7].......*arrived*......... (arrive) at Sutton Place, I had a feeling that somebody [8].....*was watching*....... (watch) me. I got out of the car and went towards Number 12.

As I [9].....*was walking*......... (walk) to the door, I [10].........*could*......... (can) hear voices in an upstairs room. But f).....*when*..... I knocked at the door, they stopped. The door was open so I decided to go in. The door closed suddenly. Somebody [11].......*was standing*........ (stand) behind me.

[to be continued]

○○○ Go for it

Past simple and continuous
Time markers *while, as, when*
Prepositions of motion

8 Look at the pictures below. Then in your notebook, write about what happened to Laura Brown. Include the following words in the box.

nouns
• rucksack • path • rocks • thunderstorm • ankle • helicopter • stretcher • hospital

verbs (past simple or continuous)
• to pack • to fall over • to break • to wave • to land • to dial 999

time markers
• while • as • when

prepositions of motion

It was a beautiful day, so Laura Brown decided to ...

9 In your notebook, write the next paragraph of the detective story in Exercise 7.

15 minutes later

Communication

Stay cool/Move on

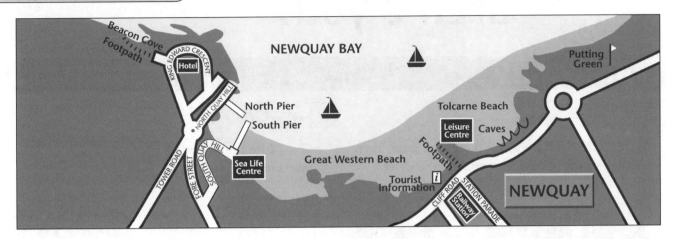

10 ⟩ Look at the map. You have just finished playing crazy golf at the Putting Green and you have decided to walk to Beacon Cove. Complete the directions.

- past • along • up (• down)
- from • down • until you get to
- turn right into • turn left

The quickest way to Beacon Cove is to go **down** to Tolcarne Beach. Then walk ¹...... *down* ...... the beach. Go ²...... *past* ...... the caves and keep walking ³...... *down* ...... the South Pier. Go ⁴...... *along* ...... South Quay Hill and ⁵...... *turn right into* ...... Fore Street. When you get to the roundabout, go straight on. You'll see a big hotel in front of you. ⁶...... *Turn left* ...... at the hotel. There's a footpath ⁷...... *from* ...... the road ⁸...... *up* ...... to Beacon Cove.

●●● Go for it

11 ⟩ Look at the map of Newquay again. You are at the Sea Life Centre. Give directions to 1) the North Pier by car and 2) the railway station on foot, via the beach. Write the conversations in your notebook using some of the prompts.

- Could you tell me the way to / where ... ?
- Certainly. / Of course.
- as far as
- on the right / left
- until you get to
- take the first turning

Conversation 1
Tourist: *Excuse me, could you tell me the way to ... ?*

❓ What's wrong?

12 ⟩ Circle and correct the mistakes.

He fell ⟨to⟩ the water. *He fell into the water.*

1 The football went throgh the window.
The football went through the window

2 Walk along this street as far to the playing fields. *as*
Walk along this street as far as the playing fields.

3 Two students, who looked out of the window at the time, saw the accident.
Two students, who were looking out of the window at the time, saw the accident

4 Excuse me. Could you tell me where is the station?
Excuse me. Could you tell me where the station is?

7 You're Nicola, aren't you?

Vocabulary

1 Complete the words for things you wear. Then write them in the correct section in the chart.

b l_ou s_e

1 je_a_n_s_
2 s_o_c_ks
3 b_o_a_ts
4 s_w_eate_r_
5 c_o_a_t_
6 sk_i_rt
7 j_a_c_k_e_t_
8 t_r_a_i_n_e_rs
9 _t_rou_s_er_s_
10 c_a_p

11 sh_i_r_t_t
12 dr_e_s_s_
13 sh_o_es
14 r_a_i_nc_o_a_t
15 ov_er_c_o_a_t
16 t_i_e
17 h_a_t_
18 s _ _ t
19 T-sh_i_r_t_
20 t_i_gh _s

Head	hat, cap	
Feet	trainers, boots shoes	
Upper part of body	**blouse**	t-shirt, tie sweater
Lower part of body		trousers, jeans socks
Whole body		

2 Write the names for the parts of Nigel's clothes.

1 *sleeve*
2 a collar
3 cuffs
4 pockets
5 hem turn up
6 laces

3 Complete the sentences using the words and phrases.

- situation comedy - jokes - satire
- cartoon - sense of humour (- slapstick)
- stand-up comedian

I know it's only **slapstick**, but I still laugh when I see somebody slip on a banana skin.

1 He's got a good ...... sense of humor ......
   He makes me laugh.

2 I never laugh at his ...... jokes ....
   I just don't find them funny.

3 There's a new film about Britain in the 1980s.
   It's a political ...... satira situation comedy ....

4 *Three's a crowd* is on every week from 7.30 to 8.
   It's a ...... satire ....

5 She performs at The Bridge Café every Friday
   night. She's a ...... stand-up comedian ....

6 Which *Batman* film do you prefer – the version
   with real actors or the ...... cartoon ...... ?

Go for it

4 Complete the leaflet for young people working in tropical climates.

Recommended clothing for work in rainforest regions

FOOTWEAR

For daily wear you will need • 1 pair of strong walking **boots**

• 1 pair of a) *shoes*

• 5 pairs of long b) *socks*

CLOTHING *occasions*

For formal occasions you will need 1 set of smart clothing. This should include:

For women • 1 knee-length cotton c) *shirt* or d) *clothes*

• 1 blouse with long e) ~~trousers~~ *blouse sleevs*

For men • 1 pair of smart f) *trousers* • 1 white g) *shirt*

You will also need casual clothing. This should include

• 1 waterproof h) *sweater* with large i) *pockets Hood*

• 2 pairs of j) *shorts* • 1 pair of denim or cotton k) *jeans*

• at least 3 cotton l) *T shirts*

apron, minimatue

Grammar

Stay cool

Question tags

5 Complete the sentences with the correct question tags.

Your aunt's the manager of the hotel, **isn't she** ?

1 You don't work at the hotel, ...*do you*.. ?

2 I'm not late, ...*do you*...... ? (*am I*)

3 You're here for the championships, ...*aren't you*...... ?

4 Tom doesn't live in London, ...*does he*.... ?

5 You and Louise went to town, ..*didn't you*? ?

6 Your journey wasn't very good, ...*was it*.. ?

7 We were standing at the same bus stop, ...*weren't we*.... ?

8 You've both been to Newquay before, ...*haven't you*.... ?

9 You aren't working late, ...*are you*...... ?

10 They weren't at the beach, ...*were they*.. ?

Present perfect simple with *just, already, yet*

6 Use the prompts to write sentences using the correct form of the present perfect simple.

We / any fish / yet / not catch

We haven't caught any fish yet.

1 He / her birthday present / not buy / yet

......*He hasnt bought her birthday present yet.*

2 play / just / Our team / a fantastic game

......*Our theam has just played a fantastic game*

3 you / yet / read / the script / ?

......*Have you read the script yet?*

4 some sandwiches / We / make / just

......*We have just made some sandwiches*

5 I / The Verve in concert / see / already

......*I have already seen The Verve in concert*

6 not show you / yet / I / my holiday photos

......*I haven't shown you holiday photos yet.*

Move on/Go for it

Past simple and present perfect simple

7 ▷ It is Friday. Use Lisa's diary entries and the prompts to interview her about her week.

7 SATURDAY
Basketball match.
We were the best team, but we didn't win.
New Ben Affleck film with Michelle - brilliant!

8 SUNDAY
Tennis in the park.
New Woody Allen film with Mum - boring.

9 MONDAY
Tickets for next Saturday's Lighthouse Family concert arrived today!

10 TUESDAY
School concert - very good!

11 WEDNESDAY
Halfway through reading 'Bad Girls' - excellent!

12 THURSDAY
Started work on History project at Mel's house.

13 FRIDAY

you / see / any films / recently?

Have you seen any films recently?

Yes, I've seen two, the Ben Affleck film and the Woody Allen film.

you / enjoy / the Woody Allen film?

Did you enjoy the Woody Allen film?

No, I didn't. It was boring.

Did 1 you / enjoy / the Ben Affleck film?

Yes I did. It was brilliant.

---

2 Which sports / you / play / since last Friday?
have ... ed

I'm played tennis, basketball

3 When / you / play / in the basketball match?
did

I played in the basketball on Saturday

4 you / win / the match?
Did

No, we didn't

5 you / receive / your tickets for the Lighthouse Family concert / yet?
Has ... d

Yes, I've received

6 you / go / to the school concert / on Tuesday?
Did you

Yes, I did

7 you / go / to the Lighthouse Family concert / yet?
Have ... ne

No, I haven't

8 you / finish / Bad Girls / yet?
Have ... ed

No, I haven't

9 you and Mel / start / your History project / yet?
Have ... ed

Yes, I have

Communication

○ Stay cool/Move on

8 Read the first paragraph of the article. Then ask and answer five questions to check the information.

Modern novelist of the moment

Name: Jenn Crowell

Place of birth: Jacobus, Pennsylvania

Age: 18

Last year, Jenn Crowell published her first novel, *Necessary Madness*. It is set in England and is about the relationship between a thirty-year-old woman and her dying husband. The novel was a huge success. Jenn has already signed a contract for her next novel. It is set in Iceland, which she is going to visit in July.

Jenn started writing when she was seven. At the age of sixteen, she went to a writers' workshop, which gave her the confidence to begin writing a novel. She wrote *Necessary Madness* in three months. 'I didn't have a plan. I didn't start at the beginning and I didn't know where I was going,' she says. But she had all the characters in her head before she started.

Jenn has just completed a publicity tour for *Necessary Madness*. She enjoys travelling, but loves going back to Pennsylvania or to her beach house in South Carolina, where she wrote part of the book.

You: (born) *Jenn, you were born in Pennsylvania, weren't you?*

Jenn: *That's right, I was.*

You: (last year) 1 *You published*

Jenn: 2 *Yes, I did*

You: (England) 3 *It's set in England isn't it?*

Jenn: 4 *Yes, it is*

You: (contract) 5 *Jenn 've already signed a contract, Haven't you?*

Jenn: 6 *Yes, I have*

You: (Iceland) 7 *It's set in Iceland, I isn't it?*

Jenn: 8 *Yes, it is*

You: (July) 9 *Jenn 're going to visit Iceland in July, aren't you*

Jenn: 10 *Yes, I'm*

○○○ Go for it

9 Read the rest of the article. In your notebook, write five more questions and answers to check the information.

? What's wrong?

10 Circle and correct the mistakes.

(I've been) to Greece three years ago.
I went to Greece three years ago.

1 You've got two brothers, isn't it?
haven't you

2 Hows it going?
Is

3 I never wear shirts with long sleves.
sleeves

4 I've done already something wrong.
already

5 I haven't heard their new single already.
yet

6 She's got a really good sense of the humour.

31

COOL FM

3 The hostel

The hostel in George Street was a large red-brick building. Scott walked up the steps and went into the reception area.

'Can I help you?' asked the receptionist.

'I've just arrived and I need somewhere to stay.'

'OK. I'll just take some details – You're in Dormitory B. Go along this corridor, through the double doors at the end and up the stairs. Dormitory B is on your left. You're sharing with five others.'

'Thanks.'

That night, as Scott was falling asleep, he heard a strange noise. He half opened his eyes. A ray of light from the window caught the silhouette of a person by his bed. It was Dean, one of the other boys in the dormitory. He was crouching on the floor and slowly pulling Scott's guitar from under his bed.

'Hey, what do you think you're doing?' shouted Scott, jumping out of bed.

'Who, me?' said Dean.

'Yes, you.'

'Nothing. I was just looking for my shoes.'

The other boys woke up.

'What's the matter, Dean?' It was Dean's friend Jason. 'Is the new boy giving you trouble?'

'Nothing I can't handle.'

Suddenly Dean leapt up and tried to hit Scott. Scott jumped out of the way, caught Dean's arm and pulled it up sharply behind his back.

At that moment, the warden, who was walking along the corridor, came into the dormitory.

'What's going on? What's all this noise?'

'He started a fight,' said Dean.

'That's right,' said Jason. 'Dean was only trying to protect himself.'

'Look, he's ripped the sleeve of my jacket,' said Dean.

The warden turned towards Scott. 'You're new, aren't you? What's your name?'

'Scott Patterson.'

'Well, Scott Patterson. We don't want this kind of thing here.'

'Just a minute. You haven't heard my side of the story yet, have you? He tried to steal my guitar as I was sleeping.'

'I'm not interested. Take your guitar and your bag and get out!'

Scott put on his clothes, picked up his belongings and left.

In your notebook, write questions for these answers.

1 Because he needed somewhere to stay.
2 He was trying to steal Scott's guitar.
3 No, he didn't, because Scott jumped out of the way.
4 Because he heard the noise in the dormitory.
5 No, he only listened to Dean's story.

You ought to try them.

Vocabulary

Stay cool

1 > Which of the cooking terms can go with each food item?

Food	grilled	boiled	fried	grated	sliced	scrambled
chicken	✔	✔	✔		✔	
1 eggs		✔	✔		✔	✔
2 fish	✔	✔	✔		✔	
3 potatoes		✔	✔			✔
4 rice		✔				✔
5 sausages	✔					
6 carrots		✔		✔	✔	
7 tomatoes					✔	

Move on

2 > Write the missing items on the menu.

BREAKFAST

❖ **S c r a m**bled egg **g s** on toast

LUNCH

❖ Vegetable curry with ¹b_o i l e d_ ri_ce

❖ Banana yoghurt

DINNER

❖ Salad of lettuce, ²sl_i c e d_ t_o a s t s_,
   ³_c h_op_p e d_ _o n_ion and crispy
   ⁴f_r i e d_ bacon

❖ ⁵Ba_h e d_ _f_ish topped with
   ⁶ma_s h e d_ _p_otatoes and
   ⁷gra_t e d_ _c h_ese

❖ Fresh fruit

Go for it

3 > Complete the questionnaire.

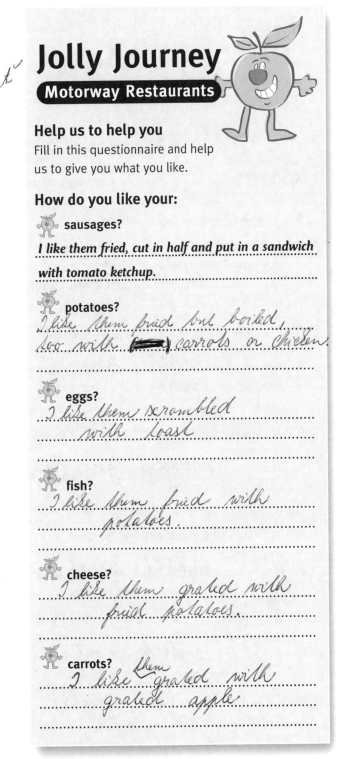

Jolly Journey
Motorway Restaurants

Help us to help you

Fill in this questionnaire and help us to give you what you like.

How do you like your:

sausages?

I like them fried, cut in half and put in a sandwich with tomato ketchup.

potatoes?

I like them fried but boiled, too. with carrots or chicken.

eggs?

I like them scrambled with toast

fish?

I like them fried with potatoes.

cheese?

I like them grated with fried potatoes.

carrots?

I like them grated with grated apple

Grammar

Stay cool

Verbs *should/shouldn't* and *ought to/ought not to*

4 > **Give advice for these situations, using the verbs in brackets.**

should/shouldn't

A: Greg's going to his cousin's wedding and he doesn't know what to wear.

B: He ***should wear*** (wear) a suit.

1 **A:** Our teacher gets annoyed when we hand in our homework late.
B: You ......*should do* .... (do) it on time.

2 **A:** My sister often puts things under the grill and goes to watch TV.
B: She ......*should leave* .... (leave) food under the grill when she goes out of the kitchen.

3 **A:** They always have arguments when they go on holiday.
B: They ......*shouldn't go* .... (go) on holiday together.

ought to/ought not to

4 **A:** He wants to lose weight but he loves chocolate.
B: He ......*oughtn't to eat* (eat) chocolate if he wants to lose weight.

5 **A:** They always stay at home and watch TV at the weekend.
B: They ......*ought to go out* (go out) and do some exercise.

6 **A:** I've got a really awful pain in my neck.
B: You ......*ought to see* .... (see) a doctor about it.

Verbs *have to* and *must*

5 > **Circle the correct word(s).**

She's never free on Sundays.
She *must* / (*has to*) visit her cousins.

1 It's OK. You *mustn't / don't have to* walk home with me after the cinema.
2 They can't go to the match because they always *must / have to* help their mother on Saturdays.
3 You *mustn't / don't have to* play loud music late at night.
4 *Must you / Do you have to* be at school by 8.30?
5 What jobs *must she / does she have to* do at home?
6 We've eaten a lot of pizza this week. We *must / have to* try to eat more fresh fruit.

Move on

Verbs *should/shouldn't* and *ought to/ought not to*

6 > **Give two pieces of advice for each situation.**

Use *should* and *shouldn't*.

A: I think I've broken my ankle.
B: ***You should go to hospital and have an X-ray.***
You shouldn't walk on it.

1 **A:** I can't afford to go to the cinema this week.
B: You should stay at home
You shouldn't go this week

2 **A:** Let's jump into the pool from the top board.
B: You should think it over
You shouldn't do it

Use *ought to* and *ought not to*.

3 **A:** We want to get a suntan.
B: You ought to got a beach
You oughtn't to go

4 **A:** I've just found a credit card.
B: You ought to
You oughtn't to

⊙⊙⊙ Go for it

Verbs *should* **and** *ought to*
Verbs *have to* **and** *must*

7 ⟩ **Complete the letter using the positive or negative form of** *should, ought to, have to* **or** *must.*

Write *in*

Have you got something on your mind?
Well, why not pick up a pen and write to us?

Linda Kelly from Manchester did.

Dear Editor,

I've just read two articles in your magazine. One was about traffic pollution and the other was about how unfit young people are. I'd like to comment on those two articles.

I *have to* be at school by 8.15. It takes me 25 minutes to walk there and I ¹ *have to* cross two busy roads. In cold, wet weather, my dad offers to take me in his car, but I say no. My friends say I ² *should* accept, but I don't agree. We ³ *ought to* stop our parents using their cars for short journeys. One of my friends only lives a short distance from school. She says she ⁴ *must* go by car because it isn't safe to walk. I've walked to school since I was eleven years old and I've never had a problem. She ⁵ *ought to* walk with me! And in Games lessons, when we *have to* run round the games field, she can't do it, but I find it easy. She's so unfit!

And another thing! Our parents ⁷ *should* walk to the local shops. They ⁸ *ought to* take the car to the out-of-town superstores. I feel very strongly about this: we ⁹ *must* stop using cars for every little journey! We ¹⁰ *mustn't* be dependent on them!

Yours angrily,

Linda Kelly
Manchester

Right on, Linda! She may be angry, but she's right, isn't she, guys? *(Mack, the Editor)*

35

Communication

8 > Use the prompts to complete the dialogues and write two new ones.

Dad: (take the dog for a walk?)
(make some phone calls)

Would you mind taking the dog for a walk, Sara? I have to make some phone calls.

Sara: (✔) *Sure. No problem.*

Sara: (✘ do my homework) *I'm sorry, but I can't. I have to do my homework.*

1 **Mum:** (get the bus to school this morning?)
(leave the house early)

Would you mind getting the bus to school this morning Jack? I have to leave the house early

Jack: (✔) *Sure. No problem*

2 **Dad:** (do the washing-up?)
(go to a parents' meeting)

Would you mind doing the washing-up, Lucy? I have to go to a parents meeting

Lucy: (✘ go to my dance class) *I'm sorry but I can't I have to go to my dance class*

3 **Jan:** (pick up the dry-cleaning after work?)
(work late this evening)

Would you mind picing up the dry cleaning after work Sue? I have to work late this evening

Sue: (✔) *Yes, sure!*

4 **Mr Lee:** (clear the table for me?)
(post some letters)

Would you mind clearing the table for me? I have to post some letters

Sophie: (✘ wash my hair) *No I'm sorry but I must wash my hair*

9 > In your notebook, write the conversation for this situation.

Lynn, the hotel manager, wants Tom to work late this evening because she has to go out. Unfortunately, Tom can't stay late because he has promised to help his mother prepare for Jamie's birthday party.

Lynn: *Tom, would you mind ... ?*

What's wrong?

10 > Circle and correct the mistakes.

Does he has to wear a uniform?
Does he have to wear a uniform?

1 Do you like white ~~slice~~ bread?
sliced

2 Would you mind ~~take~~ this book back to the library for me?
taking

3 You ~~shouldnt~~ eat just before you go swimming.
shouldn't

4 We ~~ought~~ stay in and work this evening.
ought to

Culture snapshot

Food in Britain

In many British towns and cities, you will find restaurants which serve Chinese, Indian, Japanese, Thai, Greek, Turkish, Italian, Spanish, Mexican and, of course, American-style food. Dishes which were once quite unusual in Britain, such as curry, pasta, paella, moussaka, pizza, hamburgers and kebabs, are now popular. They have become part of the British diet, along with traditional food like roast beef and Yorkshire pudding, sausages and mashed potatoes, and fish and chips.

Have any dishes from your country become popular in Britain?

9 > They've been bullying me.

Vocabulary

Stay cool

1 > Circle six more adjectives describing emotions in the wordsquare.

L	I	M	G	B	E	V	L	C	Y
D	O	V	N	E	R	V	O	U	S
E	N	A	S	T	Y	H	N	J	H
J	E	A	L	O	U	S	E	T	Y
M	I	S	E	R	A	B	L	E	W
O	T	H	H	A	P	P	Y	E	N

Now match five of the adjectives with the pictures above.

1 ...miserable... 4 ...nasty...
2 ...happiness... 5 ...nervous...
3 **lonely**

Move on

2 > Write the adjectives from the wordsquare and change them into nouns.

lonely .... *loneliness* ....

1 ...jealous.......... ...jealousy..........
2 ...miserable.......... ...misery..........
3 ...happy.......... ...happiness..........
4 ...nervous.......... ~~nervous~~ nervously
5 ...shy.......... ...shyness..........
6 ...nasty.......... ...nastyness..........

Go for it

3 > Change each adjective in the numbered sentences into a noun ending in *-ness,* and write it in the correct lettered sentence.

1 Thank you for being so *kind.*
2 You're just *lazy!*
3 I want to get *fit.*
4 Don't drive if you're *tired.*
5 He's so *untidy.*
6 We hope you will be really *happy.*

a) We wish you great ...happiness... .
b) I have to tidy his room every day. His ...untidyness.... gets on my nerves.
c) You're good at most subjects, but your ...laziness... is your weak point.
d) On the roads, ...tiredness.... kills.
e) I want to improve my ...fitness... level.
f) Thank you for your **kindness.**

Grammar

Stay cool

Would you like me to ... ?

4 > Offer to help in these situations.

Your neighbour is ill. He cannot get out to the shops.

(do) *Would you like me to do the shopping for you?*

1 Your friend is nervous because she's got a French test tomorrow. You're good at French.

(help) *Would you like me to help you with French*

2 Your friend wants to go to a big rock concert next week. Tickets are on sale today, but he's got classes all day.

(get) *Would you like me to get tickets for the concert*

3 A friend has tripped up and hurt her foot. You think she ought to go to hospital.

(take) *Would you like me to take him to hospital*

4 Your six-year-old brother is shy. He doesn't want to go to football practice alone.

(go) *W. you like me to go to football*

5 Your brother is miserable because two boys in his class have been bullying him.

(talk) *Would you like me to talk with boys to him.*

Present perfect continuous with *for* and *since*

5 > Look at Nick's notes and use the present perfect continuous with *for* and *since* to correct the facts about his life.

Job Application

Full name	Nicholas Colin Bowers
Age	18
Languages	Spanish: started at 11 Italian: started at 14
Interests	Football: second year in the college team Music: began playing electric guitar aged 15 Started band NCB a year ago
Qualifications	Driving since last October
Work experience	Became part-time waiter at Tony's Pizza Place in July

(learn Spanish / two years)

(learn) *He hasn't been learning Spanish for two years. He's been learning it for seven years.*

1 (learn Italian / three years)

(learn) *He hasn't been learning Italian for 3 years. He's been -11 - for 5 years*

2 (college football team / four years)

(play) *He hasn't been playing for 4 years He has been -11 for 2 years*

3 (the electric guitar / 13 years old)

(play) *He ... sina B... since 13...*

4 (drive / March)

(drive) *He hasn't been driving since March He's ... last October*

5 (Tony's Pizza Place / September)

(work) *He hasn't working since Sept. He has ... for in july*

38

Move on/Go for it

Would you like me to ... ?

6 > Complete the offers of help.

I wish I could windsurf like you.
__Would you like me to teach you__ how to do it properly?

1 I'm hungry.
Would you like me bring you a sandwich?

2 I haven't got anything to read.
Would you like me to borrow my magazine?

3 I'm afraid I don't know the way to your house.
Would you like me to give a map?

4 We'd love a souvenir of our visit.
Would you like me to give use a photo of you?

5 Oh no! I'm going to miss the cup final on TV.
Would you like me to watch it for you?
record video with

Present perfect continuous with *for* and *since*

7 > Look at the information below and write a profile of singer Kieran Collins using the present perfect with *for* and *since*.

	Internet
Name	Kieran Collins
Date of birth	12th April 1981
Place of birth	Dublin
Home	Dublin, then New York in 1994
Music	Guitar – age 14
Current work	Since May – album 'Jealousy' (to be released in October)
Recent interests	Learning Spanish (I've been going to classes for a few months. I'm making progress, but I don't do the homework!)

Kieran was born in Dublin on 12th April 1981. He lived there until he was a teenager. Since 1994, He has been living in N.Y. He's been playing on guitar for 8 years. He has been working on his album. He since may. He's been going to Spanish classes for a 5 months. He is making progress, but he doesn't do the H.W.

Communication

○ Stay cool

8 > Number the sentences in the correct order to make a telephone conversation.

Josie

[3] Well, that's why I'm ringing. Do you mind if I don't come this evening?

[1] Hello, Dave, it's Josie here.

[9] Yes, call me then. That'd be nice. Thanks. Bye!

[7] That's kind of you, Dave, but I don't really want to watch a video either.

[5] No, I don't really feel like reading. I just don't feel well, that's all.

Dave

[4] No, of course not. Would you like me to come over to your house? I'll bring you some magazines.

[10] Bye, Josie. See you soon.

[6] Oh, I see. Well, shall I get a video for you?

[8] OK. Shall I give you a call at the weekend?

[2] Hi, Josie! You're coming over to see me later, aren't you?

○○○ Go for it

10 > Your friend Rick needs help. In your notebook, write a conversation.

Rick's problem

> Last week I lent my dad's mobile phone to Kevin, a guy in my class. Now he won't give the phone back. For the last few days, Dad has been asking for the phone and I've been making different excuses. Kevin's been using the phone a lot and I know he's been making long-distance calls. He says I'll be in trouble if I tell my dad.

You: *You look fed up, Rick. What's the problem?*

Rick: *You know that guy Kevin at school? Well, I lent him my dad's mobile phone last week and …*

●● Move on

9 > A good friend is having a party. Use the prompts to write a conversation.

A: Offer to help with the food.
> ***Would you like me to help with the food?***

B: Refuse politely and give a reason.
> 1 **No,** ...Sorry

A: Offer to make some tapes.
> 2 ...Why like me to make some tapes

B: Accept the offer.
> 3 ...Yes, no problem

A: Ask what time the party starts.
> 4 ...What time does party start?

B: Respond.
> 5 ...About at 8 o'clock.

A: Offer to come earlier and give a reason.
> 6 ...Why l. to come earlier

B: Accept the offer.
> 7 ...Yes, O.K.

? What's wrong?

11 > Circle and correct the mistakes.

I've been (for two days feeling ill.)
I've been feeling ill for two days.

1 Are you living here for a long time?
...Has you been

2 I fear lonelyness more than anything.
....

3 Have you been waiting for long time?
....

4 I've been reading this book since three months.
...for

5 Would you like me get an extra ticket?
to ...getting

6 Its OK. Don't worry.
...It's

COOL FM

4 I'm fine.

Scott spent the rest of the night sleeping on a park bench. The next morning he was in Pitt Street Mall outside a big department store. He was playing one of his own songs. Some of the people who passed by threw a dollar or two into his guitar case. Several of them stopped to listen, which was unusual at such a busy time of the morning. While Scott was playing, he kept thinking, 'Maybe I should phone Mum. But she'll be angry with me.'

Sophie was on her way to the COOL FM studios. She was enjoying the warm summer breeze and the music. She turned to see who was playing and recognised Scott.

'Hi!' she said, when he paused between songs. 'Do you remember me? We met at the station yesterday. How are you?'

'Oh, hi!' said Scott. 'I'm fine – just fine.'

He doesn't look fine, thought Sophie. He looks lonely and unhappy.

'Are you sure?' asked Sophie.

'It's just that I've never played in the street before.'

'You look a bit down.'

'Well, if you must know, I had a bit of trouble at the hostel last night. A guy tried to steal my guitar. The warden got angry and threw me out.'

'What! He threw you out, not the other guy?'

'Yes.'

'So you've got nowhere to stay?'

'Not at the moment, no. I'll be OK, though.'

'Listen, I don't have to be at work till 9.30. I've been working really hard for the last two weeks, so they won't mind if I'm late. Let's go and have breakfast.'

They walked into a café opposite the store.

'What do you fancy?' asked Sophie.

'Oh, just a cup of coffee.'

'Come on, you can do better than that. Let me at least treat you to breakfast. How about orange juice followed by eggs, bacon, mushrooms, toast and coffee?'

'Thanks. That sounds great. I am a bit hungry.'

'You were playing really well out there. How long have you been playing the guitar?'

'Oh, since I was ten or eleven.'

'You're pretty good, you know. You ought to think about turning professional one day.'

'How would you like your eggs?' the waiter asked.

'Scrambled, please,' said Sophie.

'Fried for me, please.'

While Scott and Sophie were eating their breakfast, they talked about their favourite bands. But Scott didn't tell Sophie about his reasons for leaving home and coming to Sydney to look for Natalie.

'Would you like me to ask if there's any work for you at the radio station? We need someone to give us a hand there.'

'Well ...'

'Come on, don't be shy!'

'OK. Thanks.'

In your notebook, write if the sentences are True (T) or False (F).

1 Scott has met Sophie before. *T*
2 Scott has been in a park most of the night. *F*
3 Scott has played in Pitt Street Mall before. *F*
4 Sophie hasn't been going to work recently. *F*
5 Sophie thinks Scott should work at COOL FM. *T*

41

Reading

Television comes to St Helena

St Helena has had television since 1995. What effect has television had on people, especially young people, on the island? They were happy and friendly before TV arrived, and the children were the best-behaved in the world. Have they become violent, nasty and jealous?

A team of researchers has been trying to find the answers to these questions. Their project has not finished yet, but they have already found that young children in St Helena are at least as well-behaved now as they were before TV came to the island. And according to psychologist Dr Tony Charlton, who has been studying the effects of TV on the children of St Helena, their behaviour has actually improved: they are less likely to fight and tease each other. They have already gained 'enormous educational benefit' and the older students have enjoyed seeing the outside world for the first time, rather than reading about it or hearing about it on the radio.

We often read in the newspapers that people are violent and badly-behaved because they have seen violence and bad behaviour on TV. Television, however, has actually been contributing to the social education of the children of St Helena. It has shown them what is happening in the world and how other people live.

According to Dr Charlton, it is easier to blame TV rather than ourselves for things that are wrong in our society.

Factfile

- St Helena is a mountainous island with narrow valleys. It is in the South Atlantic Ocean between Africa and South America.
- The Portuguese explorer Juan da Nova Castella discovered St Helena on 21st May 1502. It became British in 1651.
- There are 5,644 St Helenians. Fourteen hundred of them live in Jamestown, which is the only town and port.
- Temperatures in Jamestown, the capital, range from 21°C to 32°C in summer and from 15°C to 26°C in winter.
- There are two hotels and one bank in Jamestown.
- St Helena Bay is excellent for diving. Ocean swimming is dangerous but there are some natural pools where it is safe to swim. Fishing is very popular. The best catches are barracuda and tuna – delicious grilled!

Comprehension

Stay cool/Move on

1 > Write words from the text for the definitions.

aggressive — *violent*

1 people who collect information — *is for researchers*

2 a person who studies people's minds — *psychologist*

3 got better — *improved*

4 make fun of — *tease*

5 a group of people living together — *community / tribe (society)*

2 > Complete the information with two facts for each category.

ST HELENA

Location *In the South Atlantic Ocean*
between Africa and South America

Landscape *There are two hotels and one bank in Jamestown*

Climate *tropical from 21°C to 32°C in summer and from 15° to 26°C in winter*

Population *There are 5,644 St Helenias. Fourteen hundred of them live in Jamestown*

History *Juan da Nova discovered St Helena on 21st May 1502. It became British in 1659*

Tourism *St Helena Bay is excellent for diving. Ocean swimming is dangerous but there are some natural pools where it's safe to swim*

Go for it

3 > Answer the questions.

Where is St Helena?
It's in the South Atlantic Ocean between Africa and South America.

1 When did people in St Helena first have television?
They had first television in 1905.

2 What was special about children in St Helena before that time?
~~television has actually been~~ contributing to the social education

3 What has Dr Charlton been doing in St Helena?
He has been studying effects of TV. TV on the children of St Helena

Write questions for these answers.

4 *Has this project with TV finished yet?*

No, it hasn't. It's still going on.

5 *~~What about this~~ worse? Have they been becoming ~~nastier~~ or ~~had behaved~~?*

No, they haven't. Their behaviour has improved.

6 *Why has TV been important to them*

It's been important because they've been learning a lot about the outside world.

Writing

Stay cool

4 > In your notebook, write a letter to Yasmin, a teenager in St Helena.

Ask her:

- how she spent her time before TV arrived.
- what her favourite programmes are.
- what she's been watching recently.
- what she thinks about the introduction of TV.

Tell her about the programmes you watch.

Move on/Go for it

5 > Imagine Yasmin's answer. In your notebook, write her reply to your letter.

11 > Unless I get to bed, ...

Grammar

○ **Stay cool**

Verbs *will/won't, might/might not* for predictions

1 > Complete this dialogue using *will/won't* or *might/might not* and a verb from the box where necessary.

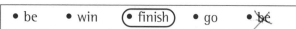

> • be   • win   (• finish)   • go   • be

Mum: What time __will__ the match __finish__ , Leon?
Leon: About six thirty.
Mum: ¹..__Will__.... you ....__be__.... home by seven?
Leon: It depends what happens after the match. You see, we ²....__might__....__go__.... to James's house to celebrate.
Mum: To celebrate? But you ³......__might__...... ...__not__...... ...__win__.... the match!
Leon: I'm sure we ⁴ ...__will Win__.... . The other team's pretty good, but we're brilliant.
Mum: I see.

Later
Mum: You're home early. What happened?
Leon: We lost.
Mum: Oh, well, never mind.
Leon: I ⁵ ...__won't__...... ...__be__.......... so big-headed in future!

First conditional: *if/unless* clause + *'ll (will)/won't*

2 > Match the sentence halves. Then write the sentences with the verbs in the correct tense.

1 If we (go) down to the beach,
2 You (not want) your dinner
3 If the food (be) spicy,
4 Unless you (book) now,
5 We (have) a barbecue
6 We (not wait) for him
7 You (not pass) your exam
8 You (not catch) the train

a) she (not eat) it.
b) unless you (study).
c) if he (not be) *isn't* here by six thirty.
d) if the weather (be) fine.
e) we (see) Jake.
f) if you (eat) all those chocolates.
g) unless you (leave) now.
h) you (not get) a ticket.

1 [e] ___If we go down to the beach, we'll see Jake.___

2 [f] *You won't wat your dinner*

3 [a]

4 [h]

5 [d]

6 [c]

7 [j]

8 [ ]

44

⦿○ Move on

First conditional: *if/unless* clause + *'ll (will)/won't* or *may/may not*

3> Use the prompts to complete the exam advice.

- ✔ have short breaks while you are revising
- ✔ feel more relaxed

- ✔ work with loud music in the background
- ✘ be able to concentrate

- ✔ have the window open
- ? work better

1 ✔ make a revision timetable
   ✘ feel stressed
2 ✔ do some physical exercise
   ✔ feel better
3 ✔ work with soft music in the background
   ? be able to concentrate better
4 ✘ leave enough time for revision
   ? not do your best in the exam
5 ✔ eat healthily
   ✔ have more energy
6 ✘ get enough sleep
   ✘ feel like working
7 ✔ spend all your time thinking about exams
   ✔ get nervous

Exam advice

If you have short breaks while you are revising, you'll feel more relaxed.

If you work with loud music in the background, you won't be able to concentrate.

If you have the window open, you may work better.

1 ....
....

2 ....
....

3 ....
....

4 ....
....

5 ....
....

6 ....
....

7 ....
....

⦿⦿○ Go for it

First conditional: *if/unless* clause + *'ll (will)*, *may* or *might*

4> Make sentences which are true for you.

if/will

If I have time this weekend, ***I'll clean my room.***

1 If I've got enough money next summer, ...
....

2 I'll stay in on Friday night if ....
....

3 If I go to the USA next year, ...
....

unless/will

Unless my parents want me to go on holiday with them, ***I'll go on a camping trip with my friends.***

4 Unless it rains on Saturday afternoon, ...
....

5 I won't go to the cinema this week unless
....

6 Unless I've got a lot of homework at the
weekend, ...

Vocabulary

Stay cool/Move on

5 Complete the words for parts of the body. Then circle the odd ones out and give your reasons.

n <u>e</u> c k   (l <u>e</u> g)   sh <u>ou</u> l <u>de</u> r

leg – the others are part of the upper body

1 fo_ _   kn_ _   e_r

2 m_ _th   h_n_   n_s_

3 _lbo_   wr_ _t   h_p

4 ba_ _   an_l_   t_e

6 Replace the words in brackets using a verb from the box in the correct tense.

• ~~arrive~~   • ~~arrive in~~   • ~~be~~   • become
• ~~buy~~   • ~~fetch~~   • return   • ~~receive~~
• change our clothes

I was (getting) worried about my trip to Paris, so I left a message on Marianne's answering machine. I [1](got) a phone call from her when I [2](got back) home after college. She's been busy because her sister's going to [3](get) married next week. My train [4](gets to) Paris at three o'clock. I have to wait for her to come and [5](get) us. I'll need to [6](get) some French francs, so I'll go to a bank as soon as we [7](get there). The plan is to go to Marianne's place first and [8](get changed), then go out for dinner.

becoming

1 .....*Received*.....   5 .....*fetch*.....
2 .....*arrived*.....   6 .....*buy*.....
3 .....*be*.....   7 .....*return*.....
4 .....*arrives in*.....   8 ...*change our clothes*...

Go for it

7 Complete the sentences using the words in the box and phrases with *'ll + get*.

> • sunburnt   • a good grade   • a newspaper
> • an invitation   (• cold)   • lost
> • ~~tired and stressed~~

If you don't drink your coffee, *it'll get cold!*

1 If you don't put some cream on, ...*it won't* ..... *you will get sun*

2 You shouldn't work so late because .....*you* ..... *will get tired and stressed*

3 Don't worry about the exam! I'm sure .....*You will* ..... *get good grade*

4 They want you to go to their wedding. I'm sure ..... *You will get an invitation*

5 I'm going to the newsagent's, so .....*I will* ..... *get a newspaper*

6 If you don't take a map, ...*You will get lost*

Communication

Stay cool/Move on

8 Fill in the missing words to make negative questions. Then choose a reply for each question from the box.

1 *Aren't* you going on holiday with your parents this year? e

2 *Didn't* you go into town last Saturday? d

3 *Haven't* you seen *Lost in Space* yet? b

4 *~~Kant~~ Aren't* going you visit Disneyland when you go to Florida next summer? h

5 *Haven't* you been to the Rock Garden Café? g

6 *Have you* you got a modem for your computer? a

7 .... you like listening to music while you're doing your homework? ☐

8 .... you going to continue learning the guitar? ☐

Replies
a) No, I've lost interest in it.
b) No, I haven't. Where's it on?
c) No, I can't concentrate properly.
d) No, I had to help in the house.
e) No, I'm going on a cycling holiday with some schoolfriends.
f) No, but I'm going to get one soon.
g) No. There's not much for vegetarians there.
h) No, I went there two years ago.

Go for it

9 You have organised a cycling and camping trip, but it isn't going well and your friend is complaining. Complete the conversation.

You can't find the campsite.

Friend: *Didn't you bring a map?*
You: *No, I'm sorry. I didn't think we needed one.*

When you find the campsite, it's full.

Friend: 1 *Didn't you booked* .... a place?
You: 2 *I ~~think~~ I didn't find it* .... necessary.

You get a puncture. *defeat* You've left your repair kit at home.

Friend: 3 *Haven't you taken some repair kit* .... ?
You: 4 *I've forget* .... at home.

You stop at a café. Your friend sits down while you buy two lemonades. There are no sandwiches left.

Friend: I'm hungry. 5 *Haven't you brought some sandwiches.* .... ?
You: 6 *No, I left them home* ....

When you come out of the café, your bikes have gone. You forgot to lock them.

Friend: 7 .... ?
You: 8 ....

Let's go home.

They were delivered today.

Vocabulary

1 > Circle ten more adjectives in the wordsquare and use them to complete the sentences.

C	A	R	E	L	E	S	S	T	A
R	U	D	E	I	D	W	E	Y	T
I	S	H	Y	J	K	I	N	D	Q
T	J	E	A	L	O	U	S	M	G
I	P	H	A	P	P	Y	I	Q	H
C	M	I	S	E	R	A	B	L	E
A	F	R	I	E	N	D	L	Y	B
L	P	O	L	I	T	E	E	V	X

You seem to like making nasty comments. Why are you so _critical_ ?

1 He's always smiling, always ....

2 He was very unhappy. He looked

....

3 She often looks after my little brother. She's

really ....

4 Come and meet some of my friends.

Don't be ....

5 He never does silly things. He's so

....

6 He's a very .... child. He always

says 'please' and 'thank you'.

7 He makes a lot of mistakes because he doesn't

check his work. He's so ....

8 She gets on well with everybody. She's a

.... sort of person.

9 She's going out with another boy and Mark's

become terribly ....

10 She walked right past him without saying 'hello'.

I thought that was ....

2 > Match the words with their definitions.

1 factory farming
2 to stack
3 hygienic
4 to flap
5 claw
6 predator
7 free-range
8 organic
9 to peck
10 straw

a) clean, free from disease
b) to put one on top of another
c) to move up and down like the movement of a bird's wings
d) an animal which hunts and eats other animals
e) produced without using chemicals
f) allowed to move around outside
g) to take a small, quick bite with a beak (used to describe the way a bird eats)
h) part of a dried plant such as wheat, used to keep animals warm and clean
i) a system which aims to get the maximum profit from animals kept for food
j) part of a hen's foot

Write the names of:

1 three animals which are predators.

....

....

....

2 two organic foods you know of.

....

....

3 one animal which is factory farmed.

....

Grammar

Stay cool/Move on

The passive: present and past simple

3 > Use a verb from the box in the passive to complete the Wimbledon website page.

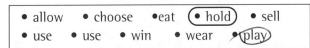
• allow • choose • eat • hold • sell
• use • use • win • wear • play

Internet

Back Forward Reload Home Search Guide Images Print Security Stop

Wimbledon is the oldest tennis championship in the world

WIMBLEDON FACTS

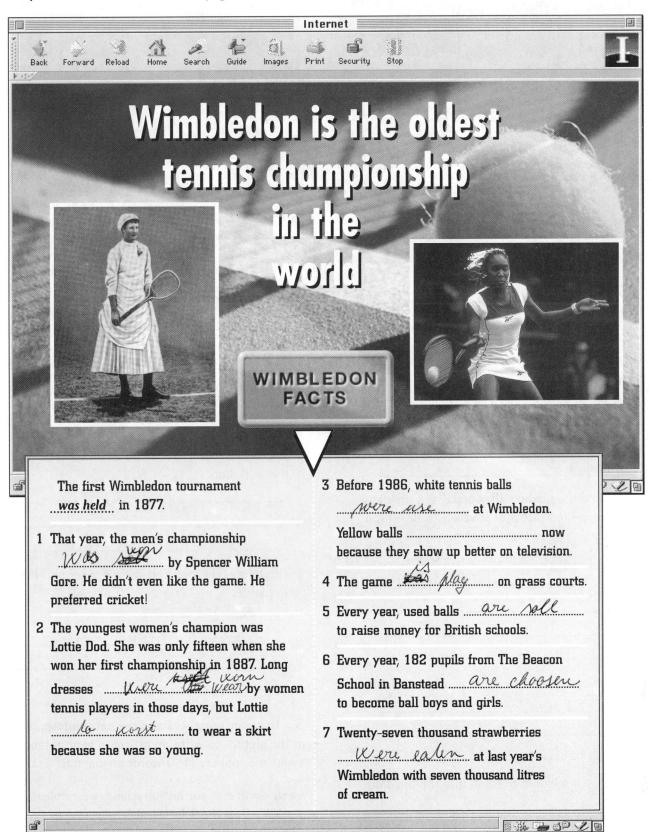

The first Wimbledon tournament _was held_ in 1877.

1 That year, the men's championship _was won_ by Spencer William Gore. He didn't even like the game. He preferred cricket!

2 The youngest women's champion was Lottie Dod. She was only fifteen when she won her first championship in 1887. Long dresses _were worn_ by women tennis players in those days, but Lottie _was allowed_ to wear a skirt because she was so young.

3 Before 1986, white tennis balls _were used_ at Wimbledon. Yellow balls .... now because they show up better on television.

4 The game _is played_ on grass courts.

5 Every year, used balls _are sold_ to raise money for British schools.

6 Every year, 182 pupils from The Beacon School in Banstead _are chosen_ to become ball boys and girls.

7 Twenty-seven thousand strawberries _were eaten_ at last year's Wimbledon with seven thousand litres of cream.

49

○○○ Go for it

Present and past simple, active and passive

Yesterday, thieves robbed the Delarte jewellery workshop.

❶ **7.00 p.m.** After weeks of careful planning, the thieves switch off the closed circuit television, place a ladder in the yard behind the workshop and climb onto the roof.

❷ **7.10 p.m.** They handcuff the manager and an employee to a table and tie scarves around their mouths.

❸ **7.15 p.m.** They put jewels worth over £1 million into bags.

❹ **7.20 p.m.** They leave the building. Nobody sees them.

4 ⟩ Change these sentences about the robbery into the passive.

Yesterday thieves stole jewels from a jewellery workshop.

Yesterday jewels were stolen from a jewellery workshop.

1 The workshop, where they make new jewellery and repair old pieces of jewellery, is in central London, close to Oxford Street.

The workshop, where is new jewellery made and repaird

The thieves handcuffed two people to a table.

Two people

They used a ladder to climb into the building.

4 According to the police, the thieves planned the robbery carefully.

....

....

5 The police found the ladder in the yard behind the workshop.

....

....

....

6 The thieves did not hurt the manager and the employee.

The manager or the imployee worent hurt.

....

5 ⟩ Use your sentences and the extra information in the picture to write an article in your notebook about the robbery (150 words maximum).

Jewels worth over one million pounds were stolen yesterday from the Delarte jewellery workshop ...

Communication

Stay cool/Move on

6 Rewrite the conversations correctly. Then match them with two of the pictures.

1

A: There's no hot water in my bathroom.
Hello. You could do something about it?

B: I sorry about that. I send someone up.

Picture ☐

Hello. There's ....

....

....

....

2

A: I afraid I have to complain about
the new receptionist. Is quite
rude and unhelpful.

B: I have a word with him.

Picture ☐

....

....

....

....

....

○○○ Go for it

7 In your notebook, write conversations for the remaining two pictures above.

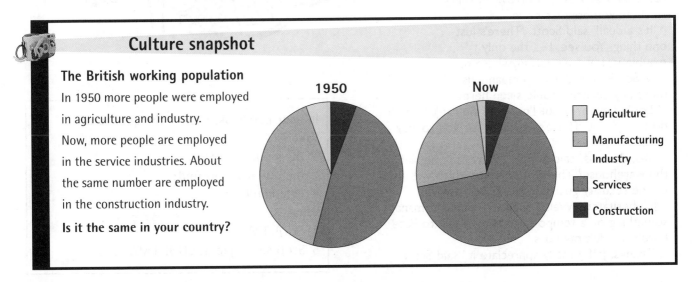

Culture snapshot

The British working population

In 1950 more people were employed in agriculture and industry. Now, more people are employed in the service industries. About the same number are employed in the construction industry.

Is it the same in your country?

1950   Now

☐ Agriculture

☐ Manufacturing Industry

☐ Services

☐ Construction

5 It's a deal!

'So, here we are.' Sophie showed Scott into the reception area of COOL FM. 'Just wait here a moment while I go and talk to the studio manager.'

'Jeff, do you remember the guy from Gosford who was interviewed for the *Welcome to Sydney* programme?'

'No, I'm afraid I don't. Why?'

'I met him by chance on the way into work this morning. He was playing the guitar in Pitt Street Mall. He knows a lot about music and he needs to earn some money. I was wondering, could we find some work for him?'

'I don't know. Maybe. If you ask him to come in, I'll have a chat with him. We certainly need some help around here.'

A quarter of an hour later, Scott was shown into Jeff's office.

'Hi, Scott! I remember you now,' said Jeff. 'I interviewed you a couple of days ago at the station. Sophie tells me that you're looking for work. We may have something for you. I don't know how much she's told you, but COOL FM is a teenage radio station. We're independent, but we're financed by advertisers. We need a studio assistant to get the discs together and put them in order, ready for the programmes. Do you think you could do that?'

'Sure. Just try me.'

'OK. I'll give you a week's trial. If you come back at 7.30 tomorrow morning, I'll show you how it's done.'

'It's a deal!' said Scott. 'There's just one thing. You see, I ..., the only trouble is, I haven't got anywhere to stay. So, do you think ... I mean ... is there any chance I could sleep here?'

'Look, I'm sorry but I'm afraid we can't let you do that, Scott. There's nowhere for you to stay here.'

'Yes, there is,' said Sophie. 'Why can't he sleep in the warehouse? There's the room which was used by the security guard. It isn't used now.'

Jeff hesitated. 'Well, I suppose we might manage something on a temporary basis. I'll talk to Pete Fordham. He's my boss.'

'Thanks, Jeff. I really appreciate it,' said Scott.

In your notebook, answer the questions.
Who is:
1 the studio manager?
2 the guy from Gosford?
3 Pete Fordham?
What is:
4 COOL FM?
5 Scott's new job at COOL FM?

13 > If I had the money, ...

Grammar

○ Stay cool/Move on

Pronouns with *some-, any-, no-, every-*

1 > **Complete the sentences using a pronoun with *some-, any-, no-* or *every-*.**

Our holiday in the country was OK, but there wasn't ...*anywhere*...... to go in the evening.

1 I can't finish my pizza. Does .... want a piece?

2 .... very funny happened to me on the way home.

3 There isn't .... near my flat to play football.

4 I've had a terrible day. .... has gone wrong.

5 We go by bus to the city centre because there's .... to park the car.

6 I'd like to correspond with .... who rides horses.

7 It's OK. I just get a bit emotional sometimes. There isn't .... wrong.

8 I'm sorry, but there's .... I can do.

9 It was a great party. .... had a really good time.

10 I've looked .... , but I can't find my watch.

11 I'd like to go .... in Scandinavia next summer.

12 I stopped at your flat on the way to the cinema, but there was .... at home.

Second conditional: *if* clause + *'d (would)/wouldn't*

2 > **Use the verbs in brackets to make second conditional sentences.**

If I _*could*_ (can) do one thing to improve life in my city, I _*wouldn't allow*_ (not allow) traffic to come into the centre. And I _*'d give*_ (give) everyone a bike!

1 If .... (he / not be) so shy, ... (he / go out) more. .... (he / not stay) at home so much.

2 **A:** If .... (you / have) the choice, ... (you / go) and live in Australia?
   B: Yes, but ....
   (I / not want) to leave all my friends.
   .... (I / take) them with me!

3 If .... (I / be) more practical, ... (I / make) things out of wood. ....
   (I / not do) it as a full-time job. ....
   (I / treat) it as a hobby.

4 **A:** If .... (you / have) the money, ...
   (you / spend) next summer travelling?
   B: Yes, but ....
   (we / not go) to England, because we've already been there.

⊙⊙⊙ Go for it

Pronouns with *some-, any-, no-, every-*

3 > In your notebook, write about your ideal holiday using at least four of the following pronouns.

> - something   • somewhere   • somebody
> - anything   • anywhere   • anybody
> - nothing   • nowhere   • nobody
> - everything   • everywhere   • everybody

in China (handwritten)

Say:

- where you would or wouldn't go.
- what sort of person you would or wouldn't go with.
- what sort of things you would or wouldn't take.
- what sort of things you would or wouldn't do.

My ideal holiday

I would go to an island somewhere in the South Pacific. I wouldn't go anywhere that was full of tourists ...

Second conditional: *if* clause + *'d (would)/wouldn't*

4 > In your notebook, write what you *would* and *wouldn't* do in these situations. Use the verbs in the box to help you, or give your own answers.

> - be really angry
> - phone for an ambulance
> - tell the manager
> - walk past
> - help him to a seat
> - (not) go and sort (them) out
> - tell him to put it back
> - not do anything
> - (not) get between them
> - (not) talk to him/her

1 If / man / badly hurt
If he / not badly / hurt
If the man was badly hurt, I'd ...

2 If I / think he / stealing it
If I / not sure

3 If / argument / serious
If / argument / not serious

4 If I / think / true
If I / not sure

Difficult situations
What would you do?

1 You're walking down the street. A man steps off the pavement and a cyclist runs into him.

2 You're in a supermarket and you see a boy putting a bottle of cola under his jacket.

3 You see two sixteen-year-old girls having an argument in the street.

4 Someone tells you your boyfriend/girlfriend is going out with someone else.

Vocabulary

Stay cool/Move on

5 Complete the word puzzle with adjectives which describe personality.

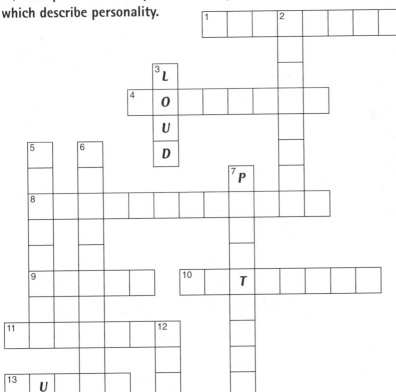

Down

2 Makes friends easily; isn't shy. (8)

3

5 Always on time; always keeps promises. (8)

6 Often bullies people. (10)

7

12

Across

1 Easily hurt by someone who is critical. (9)

4

8 Doesn't take things too seriously. (12)
9 Likes telling people what to do. (5)
10 Is always the first to talk to new people. (8)
11 Works hard and doesn't smile much. (7)
13 The opposite of 3 Down. (5)

Go for it

6 Which qualities do the following people need to do their jobs well? Use the adjectives in Exercise 5 and any others you know.

1 a nurse

A nurse should ……………………………………………

but he or she mustn't ……………………………………

2 a marketing manager

……………………………………………………………………

……………………………………………………………………

3 a builder

……………………………………………………………………

……………………………………………………………………

4 a librarian

……………………………………………………………………

……………………………………………………………………

Communication

Stay cool

7 ❯ Put the dialogue in the correct order.

1 **g** 2 ☐ 3 ☐ 4 ☐ 5 ☐ 6 ☐ 7 ☐ 8 ☐

a) I can't do that!
b) I think I'm in love.
c) If I were you, I'd send her a note and tell her.
d) Krisha. I really like her but I'm shy. What do you think I should do?
e) Volleyball? That's a much better idea. OK.
f) Well, why don't you ask her if she wants to play volleyball after school?
g) What's the matter with you?
h) Oh no, not again! Who with?

Move on

8 ❯ Make suitable suggestions for this situation.

Rosie: I found this blue and white scarf in the corridor. What do you think I should do?

Leanne: 1 ....
....

Rosie: Oh, I can't do that. If I lost a scarf like that, I'd want it back.

Leanne: 2 ....
....

Rosie: I suppose I could do that. I'm not sure.

Leanne: 3 ....
....

Rosie: Good idea!

Go for it

9 ❯ In your notebook, write a dialogue between John and Rob.

John has heard two boys in his class talking about going into town this afternoon to steal a car. He tells Rob.

John: *Did you hear what Dave and Neil were talking about?*
Rob: *No ...*

? What's wrong?

10 ❯ Circle and correct the mistakes.

If I (would have time,) I'd come with you.
If I had time, I'd come with you.

1 What do you think should I do?
....

2 If I were you, I wouldn't do nothing.
....

3 She's nice but she's very quite.
....

4 If he asked me out, I refuse.
....

5 He hates criticism. He's very sensible.
....

STUDY CORNER

Rules with *some* and *any*
1 Is anything wrong?   3 Is anyone there?
2 Is something wrong?   4 Is someone there?

Although we usually use *any-* with questions, you can use *some-* if you think the answer is going to be 'yes'. The person who asks question 2 thinks there **is** something wrong.
The person who asks question 4 thinks there **is** someone there.

Is it the same in your language?

56

14 ▷ Someone had dropped it.

Vocabulary

◐ Stay cool/Move on

1 ▷ These are all words for types of music and musical performers. Fill in the missing letters.

blu_e_s   ☐ T

s_i_nger   ☐ P

1 c _ a _ s _ c _ l   ☐

2 co _ nt _ y and
   w _ s _ e _ n   ☐

3 dr _ m _ er   ☐

4 fo _ k   ☐

5 gu _ t _ r _ st   ☐

6 h _ _ vy me _ a _   ☐

7 j _ zz   ☐

8 p _ _ n _ st   ☐

9 p _ _ k r _ _ k   ☐

10 r _ p   ☐

11 r _ g _ ae   ☐

12 r _ _ k 'n' r _ l _   ☐

13 s _ l s _   ☐

14 s _ m b _   ☐

15 s _ ft ro _ _   ☐

16 s _ _ l   ☐

17 t _ _ h n o   ☐

18 c _ n d _ _ t _ _   ☐

19 p _ p   ☐

20 v _ o l _ n _ _ _   ☐

2 ▷ Write T next to the words in Exercise 1 which are types of music and P next to the words which name performers.

◉◉◉ Go for it

3 ▷ Which of the types of music in Exercise 1 do you associate with the following?

the 1950s and Elvis Presley

rock 'n' roll

....

1 the 1960s, Aretha Franklin and Stevie Wonder

....

2 Jamaica and Britain in the 1970s

....

3 the 1980s, short spiky hair and nose rings

....

4 fast, rhythmic talking with an instrumental background

....

5 Dolly Parton and Nashville, Tennessee

....

6 Brazil and dancing

....

Grammar

Stay cool

Past perfect simple

4 Use the prompts to make sentences about the characters.

It was Jake's first time in Cornwall.
(He not be / there before)

He hadn't been there before.

1 Nicola started work in reception.
(she work / in a hotel before?)

....

....

2 Nicola was a bit tired. (She not sleep / very well)

....

3 Jake talked about the waves in Hawaii.
(Tom / never / go / to Hawaii)

....

....

4 Nicola went to the surf shop. Jake wasn't there.
(He / already / leave)

....

5 Tom was working really hard.
(He / not have / a day off since Friday)

....

....

6 Morris was angry with Nicola.
(She / be / impolite / to a guest)

....

....

7 Tom was a bit quiet. (Jake / just / walk in)

....

too many, too much, (not) enough

5 Complete the conversation with the correct form of *there is/are* and *too much, too many, (not) enough.*

Ben is staying with Laura and helping her prepare for a pasta party.

Ben: You've invited *too many* people, you know. *There aren't enough* chairs.

Laura: I know. I'd already invited everyone before I realised.

Ben: ¹.. room for everybody.

Laura: I know, but we'll manage.

Ben: And ²..
time to get everything ready.

Laura: Stop complaining and put the fruit salad in the fridge.

Ben: I can't. ³..
things in there already.

Laura: ⁴.. spoons for everybody?

Ben: I think so.

Laura: Here, I've made some lemonade. Try it.

Ben: Yuk! It's really sweet. ⁵................................
.... sugar in it.

Laura: Look, why don't you do something useful? Get the dishes and things out.

Ben: OK. But ⁶..
plates for everybody.

Laura: Well, could you go out and buy some plastic ones?

Reported requests and commands

6 Your friend is quite bossy. Write her requests.

tell

1 Phone me later.
Don't phone after 11.

She told me to phone her later. She ....

....

....

ask

2 Please make me a cup of tea.
Please don't put milk in it.

....

....

....

want

3 Can't you have a party?
I'd prefer you not to invite Emily.

....

....

....

I know! We'll leave him a message!

2 He knew where they were because

....

I'll never finish my homework!

3 I couldn't go out last night because

....

I think I'll have another chocolate.

4 He didn't want lunch because

....

I didn't put my keys in my bag.

5 I was locked out.

....

We've met before.

6 How did you know Lucy?

....

◯◯ Move on/Go for it

Past perfect simple

7 Complete the sentences using the past perfect simple.

She's already gone home.

We arrived late at Mum's office.

She'd already gone home.

Oh, why didn't we book!

1 They couldn't get into the restaurant because

....

Reported requests and commands

8 You're babysitting for some neighbours. Change these sentences into reported speech, using the verbs *tell*, *ask*, and *want*.

Don't play your music after 9.30.

They told me not to play my music after 9.30.

1 Help yourself to some food.

....
....

2 Could you help Jack with his homework?

....
....

3 Don't let Jack stay up late.

....
....

4 Please don't make too many phone calls.

....
....

5 Put the cat out, will you?

....
....

Write three more things the neighbours said to you about inviting friends round, answering the door and leaving the answering machine on. Then change them into reported speech.

6 '...,'

They ....

....

7 '...,'

They ....

....

8 '...,'

They ....

....

Communication

◯ Stay cool/Move on

9 You are leaving your friend's birthday party and are saying goodbye to her mother. Complete this dialogue.

Mother: Nice to see you again. I hope you enjoyed the party.

You: *Yes, I did. It was very good.*

Mother: Was there enough food? I hope so!

You: 1...

Mother: What did you think of the DJ? Did he play the music you like?

You: 2...

Mother: That's good. Well, I'm glad you could come.

You: 3...

Mother: Give my best wishes to your family.

You: 4...

◯◯◯ Go for it

10 Your friend invited you to stay for the weekend. It is Sunday evening, and you are about to leave. In your notebook, write the conversation using the ideas below.

- You enjoyed the weekend a lot.
- You really liked playing volleyball on the beach.
- Your friend enjoyed the barbecue on the beach in the evening.
- Your friend suggests going walking in the mountains next month.

You: *Thanks. That was a great weekend.*

Friend: *I'm glad ...*

COOL FM
104

6 Searching for you

Scott was on his way to the warehouse. He was tired, but it had been a good week. On the first morning, Jeff had shown him what to do. He had to make a list of the discs which the DJs needed, find them and put them in the right order. After that, he had to be on hand to help in the studio. The trial week had gone well and everyone was pleased with his work.

Scott had made friends with two of the sound engineers, Adam and Nick. He'd even told them about Natalie.

'I haven't a clue where she is,' he'd said. 'What do you think I should do? Do you think I should try to find her?'

'If I were you, I'd put out a call for her,' said Adam.

'What do you mean?'

'Well, Jeff does a *Lost Friends* programme on Wednesdays and Saturdays. You could put out a call on that. You never know, she might have the radio on when your call goes out.'

'Hmm, maybe. The trouble is, I don't think she's interested in me any more.'

'Scott.' It was Nick. 'Can you help Adam and me for a few minutes? We've got to test some new sound equipment for Jeff. It's a new mixing desk for live bands. Can you go and get your guitar and play us something?'

'OK,' said Scott. He fetched his guitar, tuned it and went into the recording studio.

'Stand a bit nearer the microphone,' said Nick, 'and play what you like. OK, let's go.'

I wish I could forget you, baby,
And those days of laughter and fun,
But I have to tell you – maybe
It's easier said than done.

Searching everywhere for you, ...

'What's the song called?' said Nick when Scott had finished.

'*Searching for you,*' Scott replied. 'I wrote it myself.'

'Did you? I like it. You know, if you went professional, you could earn a lot of money.'

'Oh yeah?' said Scott, not really believing him.

'Come in here and listen. You sound really good.'

'No, I think I'll get some sleep. But thanks for suggesting it. I enjoyed it.'

'He's got such a good voice,' said Adam, after Scott had left.

'Why don't we edit the track, just for fun, and play it to Jeff tomorrow?' asked Nick.

They worked on the song until about two in the morning.

'Too much treble,' said Nick.

'Not enough bass,' said Adam.

And they produced a version of the song to play to Jeff. But they didn't tell Scott.

In your notebook, put the events in the correct order.

a) Nick asked Scott to play a song.

b) Nick asked Scott to listen to the recording.

c) Nick told Scott to stand nearer the microphone.

d) Adam told Scott to put out a call for Natalie.

e) Scott told Adam and Nick about Natalie.

Reading

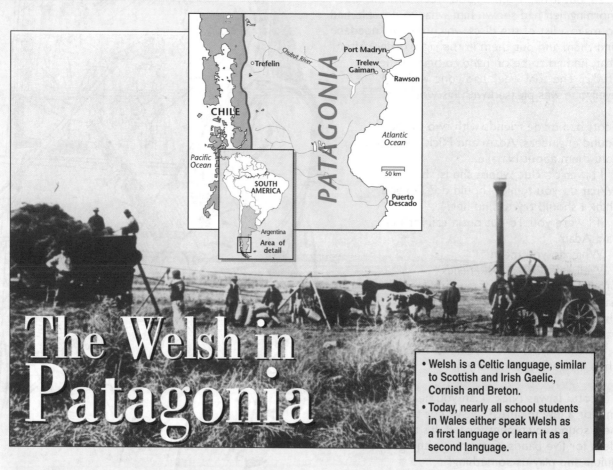

The Welsh in Patagonia

• Welsh is a Celtic language, similar to Scottish and Irish Gaelic, Cornish and Breton.

• Today, nearly all school students in Wales either speak Welsh as a first language or learn it as a second language.

In 1865 a ship called the *Mimosa* sailed from Wales in the west of Britain to Patagonia in the south of Argentina, with 153 Welsh men, women and children on board. They wanted to find somewhere far from Britain where they would be free to express their language and culture, which were beginning to disappear. They called the place where they landed 'Port Madryn'.

In the years that followed, about 3,000 other Welsh people joined them. They were given land by the Argentinian government and they were taught to hunt by the Tehuelche, native people who were friendly and helpful to them. The Welsh were called 'the bread and butter people' because they exchanged simple food for furs and skins.

The lives of the immigrants centred on the home, the school and the chapel. They were very practical people. A new currency and legal system were introduced. The land was farmed and sheep were kept on high land. Welsh was spoken everywhere. Welsh-language primary schools were set up.

In 1878 Spanish was introduced into schools, and by the turn of the century, Spanish had become the language of the classroom. As the years passed, the Welsh language fell into decline and was heard only among the older generation. They knew that if the language wasn't used by young people, nobody would understand it in a few years' time.

In 1990 Gwilym Roberts, a teacher from Cardiff in Wales, was watching a television programme about Patagonia. He discovered that the Welsh Argentine Society was looking for people to teach Welsh in Patagonia and volunteered to go.

'Patagonia is the only place in the world where the Welsh language has survived for so long away from Wales,' says Mr Roberts. 'There's something romantic about it.'

Now in Patagonia, Welsh folk music and dancing are becoming popular. 'Folk dancing isn't as skilful as the tango,' admits Sian Emlyn, the secretary of the Welsh Argentine Society, 'but it's fun.'

July 28th, the date when the Welsh first arrived in Patagonia, is a holiday. It is celebrated with tea and cakes – and, of course, bread and butter.

Comprehension

Stay cool

1 > **Read the text and find the name(s) of the following things.**

a country in South America   *Argentina*

1 a country in Britain   ....

2 a region in South America   ....

3 a type of school   ....

4 two languages   ....

....

5 a city in Wales   ....

6 a South American dance   ....

Move on

2 > **Answer these questions.**

Where is Port Madryn?

It's in Patagonia.
....

1 How did the Tehuelche help the early settlers?

....

2 Why were the settlers called 'the bread and butter people'?

....

3 Why wasn't Welsh used in Patagonian schools in the early 1900s?

....

4 Why did Gwilym Roberts go to Patagonia?

....

5 What sort of music might you hear if you went to this area?

....

6 Which does Sian Emlyn think is more difficult to learn – Welsh folk dancing or the tango?

....

7 What might you eat and drink if you were in Patagonia on July 28th?

....

Note: The photograph on page 62 shows Welsh farmers in Patagonia in the nineteenth century.

Go for it

3 > **Read the text again and make notes for these dates.**

1865 *The 'Mimosa' sailed from Wales to Patagonia.*

1865–1878

1878

1900

1990

July 28th

Communication

4 > **You have just been on a tour of Patagonia. The tour was organised by the Welsh Argentine Society. You thank the secretary of the society. Complete the conversation.**

You: That **was** a really interesting tour.
¹.................................. for organising it.

Secretary: ².................................. welcome.
I was wondering – could you write an article for our web page?

You: I ³.................................. certainly try.

Secretary: If you ⁴.................................. it to me by e-mail, I ⁵..................................
put it onto the web.

Writing

5 > **Write an article about your tour for the web page which is mentioned in Exercise 4. These are some of the things you did.**

• You visited a school where you were taught to count from 1 to 10 in Welsh.
• You went to the celebration on July 28th where you were given tea and cakes.
• You went to a festival where you tried Welsh folk dancing.

They used to hide here.

Vocabulary

○ Stay cool

1 > Complete the sentences with the correct form of the words in the box. Use each word twice.

• cook • heat • build • sing • drive

It's cold. I'll bring in the *heater* from the hall.

1 Shall I turn down the central .... ?

2 I like music but I'm not good at ....

3 Which is the tallest .... in your city?

4 Let's get the train. .... into town takes too long.

5 The .... is between the washing machine and the fridge.

6 The .... will tell you when to get off the bus.

7 Has the architect shown her new plans to the .... yet?

8 I like eating but I don't like ....

9 Dan's the lead .... in a band.

○○ Move on/Go for it

2 > Solve the crossword.

Across

1 A bird is sometimes kept in this. (4)

3 The opposite of *down*. (2)

6 Also. (3)

7 Smuggling was common two hundred years ... . (3)

9 Chemicals, acid rain and smoke cause ... of the environment. (9)

11 The number of years someone has lived. (3)

12 Please come with me, Madam. And you, too, ... (3)

13 Say again. (6)

15 Another word for *taxi*. (3)

16 The smuggled goods were disguised to ... the customs officers. (5)

18 If smugglers were caught, they were often ... to Australia. (11)

Down

1 Cornwall used to produce a lot of this metal. (6)

2 When horses run fast, they ... . (6)

4 They used to smuggle hundreds of ... of silk stockings. (5)

5 Goods which are smuggled into a country. (10)

6 It used ... be a busy port. (2)

8 The opposite of *Stop!* (2)

10 It takes longer to pack your bags than to ... them. (6)

11 The customs officer tried to ... the smuggler, but he escaped. (6)

14 It's on the side of your head. (3)

15 Smuggled goods were taken inland by horse and ... . (4)

16 England's favourite drink, which used to be smuggled into the country. (3)

17 You wear this tight-fitting hat to keep your head warm. (3)

Grammar

Verb *used to*

3 Read about Nicole Kidman and complete the conversation on the right using the verb *used to.*

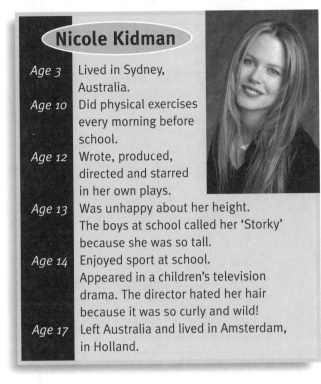

Nicole Kidman

Age 3	Lived in Sydney, Australia.
Age 10	Did physical exercises every morning before school.
Age 12	Wrote, produced, directed and starred in her own plays.
Age 13	Was unhappy about her height. The boys at school called her 'Storky' because she was so tall.
Age 14	Enjoyed sport at school. Appeared in a children's television drama. The director hated her hair because it was so curly and wild!
Age 17	Left Australia and lived in Amsterdam, in Holland.

so and *such a/an* + adjective + noun

4 What are Tom and Nicola thinking?
Complete the sentences.

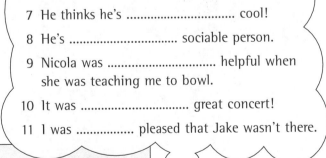

Jake is __such a__ pain at times!

1 Tom is .... kind and sensible.

2 I had .... awful day yesterday!

3 Some of the hotel guests are .... rude.

4 Morris can be .... bossy at times.

5 I was in .... bad mood after work.

6 Is Jake .... brilliant surfer?

7 He thinks he's .... cool!

8 He's .... sociable person.

9 Nicola was .... helpful when she was teaching me to bowl.

10 It was .... great concert!

11 I was .... pleased that Jake wasn't there.

A: Nicole Kidman used to live in the USA when she was young, didn't she?

B: *No, she didn't. She used to live in Australia.*

A: She was quite lazy as a child, wasn't she?

B: 1 ....
....

A: But she wasn't interested in the theatre or the cinema, was she?

B: 2 ....
....

A: She's always been happy with her appearance, hasn't she?

B: 3 ....
....

A: *Did she use to have a nickname at school?*

B: Yes, the boys called her 'Storky'.

A: 4 ....

B: Yes, she did. She used to enjoy all sports.

A: 5 ....

B: No, it used to be very curly.

A: 6 ....

B: Yes, that was just after she left Australia.

so and *such* with a clause of result

5 Match the sentences and join them using *so* or *such* and a clause of result.

1 She's been very busy.

2 I was really thirsty.

3 He was very tired.

4 It was a very boring film.

5 They had a really good holiday.

6 I'm very hungry.

a) I could eat two pizzas.

b) He went to bed as soon as he got home.

c) We left after ten minutes.

d) She hasn't had time for lunch.

e) They're planning to go again next year.

f) I drank a litre of water.

1 **d** *She's been so busy that she hasn't had time for lunch.*

2 ☐ ....

3 ☐ ....

4 ☐ ....

5 ☐ ....

6 ☐ ....

○○○ Go for it

**so and *such* a/an + adjective + noun
Verb *used to***

6 Use the information to write a paragraph in your notebook about British teenagers in the seventies. Include *used to* and *didn't use to*. Use *so* and *such a/an* to give your opinion. The words in the box will help you.

In the seventies, the clothes were so unusual/interesting. People used to wear ...

• interesting	• unusual	• colourful
• awful	• amazing	• marvellous
• important	• wonderful	
• powerful	• ugly	

• voice	• singer	• group
• music	• influence	

Seventies style

Clothes
Flared trousers, platform shoes, tank tops, ripped T-shirts, black plastic bags with chains

Hair styles
Very long, or spiky and coloured

Music
David Bowie, Bob Marley, punk, not folk music

Attitudes
Political (e.g. Rock against Racism, the Women's Movement); not as outgoing as people in the sixties

Communication

Stay cool

7 You're in London with your family. You want to take a boat trip. Complete the conversation using details of your own family.

You: (Ask for your tickets.)
1 ....
tickets to Waterloo Bridge, please?

Assistant: Certainly.

You: (Ask the price.)
2 .... ?

Assistant: £4.50 for adults and £2.00 for children under 14.

You: (Ask about special rates for students.)
3 .... ?

Assistant: Yes. For students, it's £2.50.

You: (Say how many tickets you want for adults, students and children.)
4 ....
....

Assistant: Can I see your student card(s), please?

You: (You haven't got it/them with you.)
5 ....
....

Assistant: I'm sorry, but you have to have a student card to get a reduction.

You: Oh, OK.

Assistant: Here you are. That's 6 ....
altogether, please.

Move on/Go for it

8 You and your family want to go to the Museum of the Moving Image. Read the information and write the dialogue in your notebook.

MOMI

Admission
£5.50 (18 and over), £3.50 (under 18)
Children under 5 years: free

Family tickets:
Two adults and one child (5–17) £10.50
Each additional child: £2
Children under 5 years: free

Café
Choose from a selection of food at our riverside café.

You: (Greet the assistant and ask about the price of the tickets.)

Assistant: (Give the prices. Ask how many tickets.)

You: (Respond.)

Assistant: (Say how much the ticket(s) will be.)

You: (Thank the assistant and ask about somewhere to have lunch.)

Assistant: (Respond.)

What's wrong?

9 Circle and correct the mistakes.

Can I (take message)?
Can I take a message?

1 I haven't played tennis for such long time.

....

2 I like the songs but I don't like her sing.

....

3 When I was younger, I was used to go to Blackpool for my holidays.

....

4 My grandfather use to work in a coal mine.

....

5 The weather was so hot than we stayed inside.

....

Culture snapshot

The Thames

The River Thames runs through the centre of London, past famous landmarks such as the Tower of

London and the Houses of Parliament. Tourists enjoy boat trips along the Thames, and people who live or work in London are beginning to use river transport more than they used to.

Does a river run through the centre of your capital city? Who uses it?

17 He said he'd been away.

Grammar

○ **Stay cool**

Reported statements

1 > Change these statements into reported speech.

'I'm a bit fed up.'

She said *she was a bit fed up.*

1 'We work at The Cliff Hotel.'

They said ....

2 'I'm waiting for a phone call.'

He said ....

3 'I didn't enjoy the disco.'

She said ....

4 'We've been on a boat trip.'

They said ....

5 'I'll turn the music down.'

He said ....

6 'I can't stop hiccupping!'

She said ....

2 > These students talked about their intentions for the next school year. Report what they said.

❶ Justin: 'I want to communicate more with my parents. We don't talk much.'

❷ Anthony: 'I didn't get good marks in my Maths exam. I can do better.'

❸ Leanne: 'I haven't achieved much this year. I plan to use my time better.'

❹ Alexa: 'I spend too much money. I'm going to start saving.'

❺ Brandon: 'I'm going to join a football team. I need to do more sport.'

❻ Sara: 'I'm a bit shy. I'll try to be more outgoing.'

1 *Justin said he wanted to communicate more with his parents. They didn't talk much.*

2 ....
....
....

3 ....
....
....

4 ....
....
....

5 ....
....
....

6 ....
....
....

Reported statements

3 > Pete has received a postcard from his friend Tony in Australia. In your notebook, copy and complete the postcard. Write the words Tony actually wrote.

Tony said he'd been travelling in the Northern Territory for a week. He'd started his journey in Alice Springs.

Alice Springs had been really disappointing. He'd only seen Ayers Rock from the plane but he'd go back one day to see it properly. He was in Darwin at the moment and he'd send another postcard next week from the Great Barrier Reef.

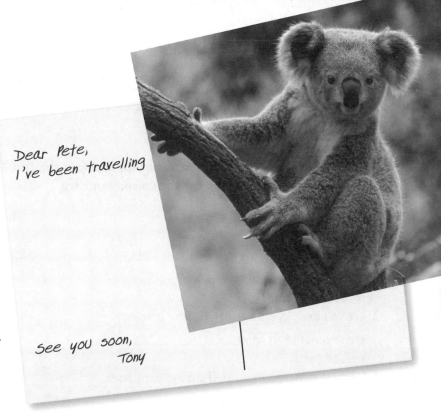

Dear Pete,
I've been travelling

see you soon,
Tony

Reported statements

4 > Read these people's impressions of London and write a newspaper article about them in your notebook. Use *say*, *tell* or *think* when introducing what they said.

The first person I interviewed was Deanne from Portland, Oregon, USA.
She said she was in London … .
Then I spoke to Karin. She thought that …

'I'm here with a friend. We're having a great time. We won't want to leave!'
Deanne, Portland, Oregon, USA

'We're hoping to find jobs here. But we haven't made up our minds how long we'll stay.'
Justin and Greer,
Johannesburg,
South Africa

'English boys are so unemotional, but they're quite friendly.'
(Karin)
'We don't like the grey river, but we love the street life of the capital.'
(Manuela)
Karin and Manuela, Trento, Italy

'We've been learning English for seven years, but we haven't been to England before. We've spoken to a lot of people and everybody's been very kind.'
Yin Wing, Wang Hsiao Mei and Ho Wing Yan, Hong Kong, China

Vocabulary

○ Stay cool

5> In each pair of sentences, use one of the words in the first sentence to make a new word for the second sentence.

This machine receives radio signals.
It's a _receiver_.

1 It's important to do some exercise.

You must understand the .... of doing exercise.

2 We've hired an entertainer for the party.

We're organising some .... for the party.

3 He isn't nervous about performing on stage.

He isn't nervous during a ....

4 The telephone was invented by Alexander Graham Bell.

His .... changed the way we live.

5 The police demonstrated how the hut was broken into.
We were given a .... of how the hut was broken into.

6 I don't speak French and Natalie doesn't speak English, so we found it hard to communicate.

There were .... problems.

○○ Move on/Go for it

6> Solve the puzzle to find the mystery word.

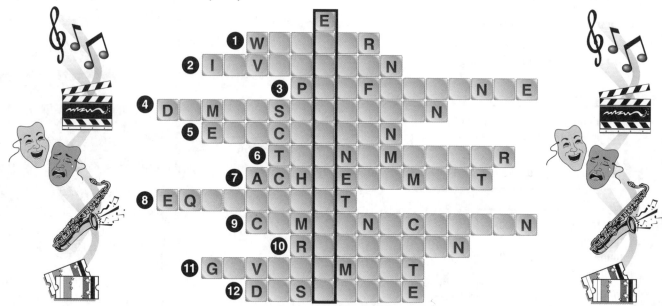

1 The person who comes first in a race.
2 A machine that is completely new.
3 A musician or an actor gives this.
4 The act of showing someone how to do something.
5 You get this at school and college.
6 A machine which sends signals.
7 Success in doing something.

8 The items which you can hire or buy to go skiing.
9 Using words or signals to send messages.
10 Someone who has a connection to your family.
11 The people who decide what happens in a country.
12 The number of kilometres between one place and another.

The mystery word is ....

Communication

○ Stay cool/Move on

7 ⟩ Rewrite the dialogue in the correct order.

Alex	Tanya
• I don't know. He didn't say. Can I take a message? • I'm afraid he's out. • OK. I'll tell him you called. • (Hello.) • It's Alex. I'm a friend of Sanjay's.	• Oh, I see. Can I speak to Sanjay, please? • Hello. Who am I speaking to? • Thanks. Bye. • When will he be back? • No thanks, it doesn't matter. I'll ring back later.

Alex: *Hello.* ....

Tanya: ¹......................................

....

Alex: ²......................................

....

Tanya: ³......................................

....

Alex: ⁴......................................

Tanya: ⁵......................................

Alex: ⁶......................................

....

Tanya: ⁷......................................

....

Alex: ⁸......................................

Tanya: ⁹......................................

○○○ Go for it

8 ⟩ In your notebook, write the conversation for the following situation.

- A friend of your mother's rings to speak to your mother. You're not sure if she's in. You check.
- She isn't in, so you offer to take a message.
- The friend says she'll ring back later.
- The friend phones again. This time your mother is on the balcony of your flat.
- You go to the window and call her.

You: *Hello, ...*
Friend: ...

? What's wrong?

9 ⟩ Circle and correct the mistakes.

Can you give me a (demonstracion) of how it works?

Can you give me a demonstration of how it works?

1 I haven't made up yet my mind.

....

2 I told that I couldn't read his writing.

....

3 They said they come next Friday.

....

4 Joe said he'd phoned but he couldn't get throw.

....

STUDY CORNER

Verbs and nouns

When you look up a verb in your dictionary, find out whether a noun can be formed from it. Note any spelling changes.

> **de·scribe** /dɪˈskraɪb/ *verb* (*present participle* **describing**, *past* **described**) to say what someone or something is like
>
> **de·scrip·tion** /dɪˈskrɪpʃn/ *noun* an account of what someone or something is like

10 ⟩ Write the nouns which come from the following verbs. They end in *-ment, -ion, –ing, -er* or *-ance.*

amuse	*amusement*	
employ	*employment*	*employer*
1 appear	....	
2 argue	....	
3 compose	....	
4 climb	....	
5 invite	....	
6 perform	....	
7 introduce	....	

COOL FM

7 This is Natalie.

'Jeff, have you got time to listen to this?' asked Adam.

'What is it?'

'It could be the next Number one, that's all.'

Jeff smiled. 'OK, I've got a few minutes.'

Later that morning, Jeff asked Scott to come up to the studio, just before he started the *Lost Friends* programme.

'Adam's been telling me about Natalie. Do you want me to put out a call for her?'

'Yes, please.'

'And is there a special song I should play?'

'Perhaps you could play *Truly, madly, deeply* by Savage Garden. It used to be one of her favourites.'

'OK, make sure it's with the rest of the discs. I'll play it at the end of the programme, at about 12.20.'

'Thanks, Jeff.'

Scott gave the *Lost Friends* playlist and the discs to Jeff, and then went into the reception area to listen to the show. He could hardly wait until 12.20!

Jeff removed *Truly, madly, deeply* from the pile of discs and replaced it with the new recording of *Searching for you*.

'Well, it's nearly the end of the programme. We've got time for one more request. This one's from Scott, who's "searching for you", Natalie. So if you're listening, Natalie, the number's 0161 6161.'

Scott sat and listened in astonishment. This was the song he had sung in the studio the previous evening! And it sounded so good! But he had asked Jeff to play *Truly, madly, deeply*. What was going on?

Jeff called Scott into the studio. The song finished and the phone rang.

'Hello,' said Jeff.

'Hello,' said the voice on the other end, 'this is Natalie.'

'Hi, Natalie. I've got somebody here who wants to talk to you. Hold the line and I'll put him on.'

In your notebook, answer the questions.

1 How does Jeff know about Natalie?
2 Why does Scott request *Truly, madly, deeply*?
3 What did Jeff say to Scott about playing *Truly, madly, deeply*?
4 Why was Scott surprised when Jeff played the song for Natalie?
5 What did Jeff tell Natalie when she phoned the studio?

18 ▷ 'The Birds'

Vocabulary

○ Stay cool

1 ▷ **Number the time expressions in order from the most recent to the furthest away in time.**

a) a couple of days ago ☐
b) a few days ago ☐
c) a couple of minutes ago ☐ **1**
d) several hours ago ☐
e) about a quarter of an hour ago ☐

2 ▷ **Fill in the missing letters.**

There were l **o** **a** d **s** of people queuing for the concert.

1 S _ v _ r _ l of my friends didn't get tickets.
2 There were a f _ _ problems with the sound system.
3 A c _ _ p _ e of girls in the front row walked out during the first act.
4 Then l _ t _ of people left.
5 At the end, there were only a _ o _ t ten of us in the audience!

○○ Move on/Go for it

3 ▷ **Complete the conversations. Include the following expressions of time and quantity.**

- a couple of minutes   • for ages   • lots of
- for some time   (• loads of)
- about a quarter of an hour ago

It's August 4th and Kate is having a birthday barbecue. She's just bought two hundred sausages.

Mum: Will there be enough food?
Kate: *Yes, don't worry. I've bought loads of sausages.*

1 They haven't used the barbecue since June.

Kate: Is the barbecue OK?
Mum: I don't know. ....
....

2 It's 7 o'clock. Kate's father went out at about 6.45. Her mother wonders where he's gone.

Mum: Where's your father?
Kate: ....
....

3 Kate's friend Tim wants a milkshake. Kate can make one in two minutes.

Tim: I'd love a milkshake.
Kate: ....
....

4 Kate meets Jan, who she hasn't seen since she was ten years old.

Jan: Hello!
Kate: ....
....

5 At least fifty people have come to the barbecue. Kate is really pleased. Tim comments on how many people are there.

Tim: Great barbecue. ....
....
Kate: Thanks. I'm glad you're enjoying it.

73

Grammar

Stay cool

Reported questions

4 > Change these direct questions into reported questions.

Where do you come from?
She asked him _where he came from._

Are you waiting for the 53 bus?
He asked her _if she was waiting for the 53 bus._

1 Are you in Newquay on holiday?
He asked her ....
....

2 What time did you arrive?
He asked her ....
....

3 When are you starting work?
She asked her ....
....

4 Do you fancy going for a bike ride?
She asked her ....
....

5 How long have you been in Newquay?
He asked him ....
....

6 Have you ever been to South Africa?
He asked him ....
....

7 Can you do me a favour?
She asked him ....
....

8 Did you enjoy the disco the other night?
He asked her ....
....

9 Are the beaches better than the ones in Hawaii?
She asked him ....
....

10 Why hasn't he kept in touch?
She asked her ....
....

5 > Can you remember who asked the questions and who they were talking to?

Nicola asked Jake.
Jake asked Nicola.

1 ....
2 ....
3 ....
4 ....
5 ....
6 ....
7 ....
8 ....
9 ....
10 ....

The answers are at the bottom of page 79!

○○ Move on/Go for it

Reported questions
Reported statements

6 > Read the survey and answer the interviewer's questions.

HOME LIFE

1 Have you ever had a serious row with your parents?

....

2 Can you do what you want at home?

....

EDUCATION

3 Do you enjoy school life?

....

4 How important is a good education?

....

PERSONAL VIEWS

5 What sort of things do you worry about?

....

6 Who are your heroes?

....

THE FUTURE

7 Will you get a job as soon as you leave school?

....

8 Are you planning to get married and have a family?

....

Now report the questions and your answers.

1 *She asked if I had ever had a serious row with my parents. I told her ...*

....

....

2 ....

....

....

....

3 ....

....

....

....

4 ....

....

....

....

5 ....

....

....

....

6 ....

....

....

....

7 ....

....

....

....

8 ....

....

....

....

Communication

7 ⟩ Circle the correct options.

May I (put) / to put the TV on?

Yes, of course. Go straight on / (ahead.)

1 **A:** Is it all right that / if I use the phone?
   B: Yes, of course.
   A: I have to ring Sam. He asked me if I did want / wanted to go out this evening.

2 **A:** Do you mind that / if I open the window?
   B: Yes / No, not at all.

◐◐ **Move on**

8 ⟩ Write the dialogues.

   A: (make a sandwich)

   Is it OK if I make a sandwich?

   B: (✓)

   Yes, of course. Go ahead.

   (✗) (no bread)

   I'm sorry, I'm afraid there's no bread.

1 **A:** (put on / a video)

   ....
   ....

   B: (✗) (video player / broken)

   ....
   ....

2 **A:** (read / your newspaper)

   ....
   ....

   B: (✓)

   ....

3 **A:** (borrow / your tennis racket)

   ....
   ....

   B: (✗) (match at 6.30)

   ....
   ....

◐◐◐ **Go for it**

9 ⟩ Use the pictures and prompts to write a dialogue.

It's a cold winter's day. You're travelling by train to see some friends for the weekend. You've switched off your mobile phone because the battery is very low. You're reading. A woman gets into the compartment and sits opposite you.

Complete the conversation.

smoke

Woman: ¹ *Do you mind if* ....

You: ² ....

   ....

window

Woman: ³ ....

   ....

You: ⁴ ....

   ....

mobile phone

Woman: ⁵ ....

   ....

You: ⁶ ....

   ....

Woman: Well, goodbye. Have a nice journey!

You: ⁷ ....

He's too good to fall.

Grammar

Stay cool

too + **adjective** + *to*
Adjective + *enough*

1 Use the adjectives to write two sentences for each picture.

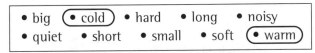

- big • cold • hard • long • noisy
- quiet • short • small • soft • warm

The water's **too cold.**

It isn't warm enough.

1 The waves ....

....

2 This tie ....

....

3 This butter ....

....

4 This beach ....

....

Verb + infinitive/gerund (-ing form)

2 Complete the sentences using the verbs in brackets in the correct form.

I want **to go** (go) to college when I leave school.

1 We agreed .... (be) home by ten thirty.

2 I've finished .... (paint) my room.

3 Try to avoid .... (travel) during the busy part of the day.

4 She refused .... (meet) him.

5 You promised .... (write) to me.

6 I hate .... (stand) in queues.

7 I'm going to give up .... (eat) meat.

8 I don't mind .... (share) a room.

◯◯ Move on/Go for it

too + adjective + to
(not) + adjective + enough to

3 > Nigel had a bad day yesterday. Look at the pictures and say what happened. Use the adjectives with *too* or *enough* and match them with the phrases.

busy   compete in the race
fit   see the film
hot ──┐   see him
old   do his homework
tired ──┘   drink

His coffee **_was too hot to drink._**

1 He ....
....
....

2 He ....
....
....

'Sorry, Nigel. I've got so much to do this evening ...'

3 His girlfriend ....
....
....

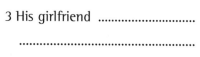

4 He ....
....
....

Verb + infinitive/gerund (*-ing* form)

4 > Use suitable verb phrases to complete the letter from a Spanish girl working in St Ives in Cornwall to her cousin in London.

Dear Melissa,

It's great here in St Ives. I'm enjoying **working** as an au pair! I take the children to school in the morning and then I help in the house. I've offered ¹... lunch every day, but Mrs Simpson said she would do it.

I've decided ²... to English classes at the local college in the afternoons. I want ³... my English quickly, and I think this is the best way. I enjoy ⁴... English. But I sometimes miss ⁵... Spanish!

I managed ⁶... tickets for the Placebo concert at Wembley Arena last week. I've got a couple of their CDs, and I really enjoyed ⁷... them live. I hope ⁸... to more concerts while I'm here.

I expect ⁹... here until the beginning of September. I hope we can arrange ¹⁰... before I go home.

Love,

Elena

Vocabulary

Stay cool

5 Circle six more 'strong' adjectives in the wordsquare and match them with the neutral adjectives below.

R	I	J	D	B	K	F	T	N
S	E	N	O	R	M	O	U	S
T	E	R	R	I	F	I	E	D
A	X	G	R	L	R	A	D	M
R	H	U	T	L	S	B	K	O
V	A	G	C	I	F	E	A	L
I	U	Y	I	A	V	D	E	P
N	S	O	U	N	B	T	K	V
G	T	R	S	T	I	N	Y	A
T	E	R	R	I	B	L	E	T
L	D	W	Q	U	K	C	H	I

    big   *enormous* ....

1 bad   ....

2 hungry   ....

3 small   ....

4 tired   ....

5 good   ....

6 afraid   ....

Move on

6 Complete each sentence with an adjective from the wordsquare in Exercise 5.

1 I was frightened. In fact, I was ...*terrified*............ .

2 I haven't eaten since yesterday.

   I'm ....

3 My room at the hotel was ten metres long by

   ten metres wide. It was ....

4 The boy kept falling asleep.

   He was ....

5 The weather was grey and wet the whole time.

   It was ....

6 I always feel hungry when I've eaten at that

   restaurant. The portions are ....

Go for it

7 Complete the conversation using adjectives from Exercise 5.

Tim: That was a very ..*good*.. concert. Did you enjoy it?

Ann: I certainly did. It was [1]............................... !

Tim: Let's go and have something to eat.

   Are you [2]...................................... ?

Ann: Yes, but I'm not [3]...................................... . Maybe we could have some fish and chips or something.

Tim: You've had a very long day. You must be

   [4]...................................... .

Ann: I'm a bit [5]............................... , it's true.

Tim: OK, let's go to The Smugglers' Cove.

Ann: Oh, no, not there. It's a [6]............................... place. The chips are always cold and the portions are [7]...................................... !

Tim: What about a pizza?

Ann: Sounds good to me!

Answers to Exercise 5 on Page 74.

Jake asked Nicola.

Nicola asked Jake.

1 Jake asked Nicola.

2 Tom asked Nicola.

3 Louise asked Nicola.

4 Nicola asked Louise.

5 Tom asked Jake.

6 Jake asked Tom.

7 Nicola asked Tom.

8 Jake asked Nicola.

9 Nicola asked Jake.

10 Nicola asked Louise.

Communication

Stay cool/Move on

8 Circle the best response in each case.

Take care. — I hope so. / (I will.)

1 See you next year. — Thanks. Same to you. / I hope so.

2 Write to me. — I hope so. / OK. I will.

3 Don't work too hard! — I hope so. / Don't worry, I won't!

4 Have a nice time. — I'm sure I will. / I hope so.

5 I hope you get good results in your exams. — Yes, so do I. / Yes, I will.

STUDY CORNER

English in everyday life

How can you read, write, listen to or speak English in everyday life? You can:

- read English magazines. ☐
- visit English-language websites on the Internet. ☐
- go to English-language films. ☐
- listen to English-language cassettes. ☐
- .... ☐
- .... ☐

Tick the things you have done in the last month. How can you improve your knowledge of English? Add to the list above if you can.

Go for it

9 Complete your part of the conversation.

You've just spent a couple of weeks staying with some family friends in Britain. You've had a really good time.

You: The taxi's here – time to go!

Friend: Unfortunately!

You: ¹ .... time.

Mother: It's been a pleasure.

You: ² ....
A-level exams.

Friend: Thanks. I'll need it!

You: ³ .... too hard.

Friend: I'll try not to.

You: ⁴ .... holiday.

Father: Thanks, I'm sure we will. Give our regards to your parents.

You: ⁵ ....
And you must ⁶ ....
some time.

Mother: That's very kind of you.

You: Bye!

Friend: Bye!

What's wrong?

10 Circle and correct the mistakes.

I was (exausted) after the race.
I was exhausted after the race.

1 'Have a nice trip.' 'Thanks. I'm sure I'll have.'
....

2 I was to tired to go out last night.
....

3 I avoid to eat too many sweet things.
....

4 She managed finish the letter before she went out.
....

5 Give my regard to your parents.
....

8 Fame at last!

'OK, that's it for today,' said Jeff at the end of the programme. Remember to tune in again on Wednesday.'

Scott and Natalie were still talking on the phone.
  'But what are you doing in Sydney?' asked Natalie.
  'I came to look for ...,' Scott hesitated, 'a job.'
  'I've missed you.'
  'You said in your letter that you wanted to start a new life in Sydney.'
  'I know, but I've realised it's not as easy as that.'
  'I've missed you, too – a lot. When can we get together?'
  Natalie said she would come to the COOL FM studios on Friday evening.

While Scott was talking to Natalie, the phone rang in the main office. Sophie answered.
  'Hello, COOL FM. Sophie Novak speaking. Can I help you? – I'm sorry, Jeff's in the studio at the moment. Oh, just a minute. He's just finished. I'll get him for you. Who shall I say is calling? – Jeff, it's Leon Cougar from Orange Records on line two. He asked if he could speak to you,' said Sophie.
  'OK, I'll take it in my office.'
  'Jeff, it's Leon. I've just heard a song called *Searching for you* on your show. What do you know about it?'
  'It was written by one of the people who works here, Scott Patterson. It's quite good, isn't it?'
  'Quite good? It's excellent! I'd like to talk to him.'
  Jeff put down the phone and went to find Scott.
  'Scott, Leon Cougar phoned a few minutes ago. He's the head of Orange Records and he happens to be a friend of mine. He heard your song on my show this morning and he'd like to talk to you. I said you'd go to his office on Friday morning at 10.30.'
  'Do you know what he wants to talk about?'
  'I'm not sure. You'd better go and find out!'
  'OK. Is it all right if I take Friday morning off?'
  'Yes. But make sure you come back. I've been talking to my boss. We can offer you a permanent job as a studio assistant, if you'd like it.'
  Scott couldn't believe his luck.

On Friday, Scott went to see Leon Cougar. After the meeting, he finally decided to phone his mother.
  'Mum, it's Scott. Look, I'm sorry I left like that, but guess what! I've got a job in Sydney and I may even get a recording contract with Orange Records! I'd like to come home tomorrow to tell you about it.'

That evening, Natalie came to the studio, where they were having a party for Scott. Sophie and Jeff came over to join them. 'Fame at last, Scott!' said Sophie. 'I think *Searching for you* is good enough to be a Number one.'
  'Thanks, Sophie,' said Scott. 'You're too kind. But don't worry, I'll always remember how it all started with an interview for COOL FM!'

In your notebook, put the events in the correct order.
a) Natalie arrives at the COOL FM studios.
b) Jeff offers Scott a permanent job.
c) Scott goes back to Gosford.
d) Scott has a meeting with the head of Orange Records.
e) Scott phones his mother.
f) Natalie and Scott arrange to meet.

Reading

A new century

An international exhibition

The Paris International Exhibition of 1900 was held to celebrate the beginning of the new century. It was the biggest exhibition Europe had ever seen. Special trains brought millions of people from all over France and other European countries to see all the latest inventions. When the visitors got to the exhibition, they were transported along moving walkways and taken to displays from all corners of the world.

Raymond Abescat was nine years old when he visited the exhibition. 'It really opened my eyes. It gave me the desire to travel.'

One of the highlights of the exhibition was the Palace of Electricity, with its hall full of lamps, generators and motors, and its grand façade lit up at night. Raymond thought it was wonderful. 'At home,' he said, 'we used oil lamps and candles – we didn't have electricity.'

Communication

Communication was becoming easier every day. The invention of the **telegraph** meant that news from all over the world was published in newspapers as soon as it happened.

By 1900 one in every fifty people in the United States had a **telephone**. If you wanted to telephone someone, you could look up their number in the telephone directory. But according to Elmie Steever, who worked at a telephone exchange in Nebraska, 'lots of times people used to just pick up the telephone and say, "Give me Mr or Mrs so and so".'

Transport

Before 1900 people travelled by horse, bicycle, boat and train, but most often on their own two feet. In 1900 the first **electric tram** appeared on the streets of New York and the first French underground railway, the **métro**, opened in Paris. But the new vehicle that everybody wanted to try was

the **motor car**. The first petrol-driven car for sale to the public was produced in Germany in 1886 by Karl Benz. It had three wheels and its top speed was about fifteen kilometres per hour. By 1900 the four-wheeled car was common.

Comprehension

Stay cool

1 > Read the text and find words which mean the same as the following:

a group of displays
exhibition ....

1 most recent

....

2 taken from one place to another

....

3 strong wish

....

4 most important parts

....

5 machines for producing electricity

....

6 front of a building

....

7 a book of telephone numbers

....

8 usual

....

Move on/Go for it

2 > Write the questions.

How did people travel to the Paris Exhibition? ....
By special trains.

1 ....
From all over France and other European countries.

2 ....
To see all the latest inventions.

3 ....
....
Because he didn't have electricity at home.

4 ....
....
It was important because it meant that newspapers got stories as soon as they happened.

5 ....
The electric tram and the métro.

6 ....
....
In 1886.

Writing

3 > Imagine that the year is 2020. In your notebook, write an article about the last day of the twentieth century and the first day of the twenty-first century.

Write about:
- the celebrations.
- communication.
- transport.

Communication

4 > You and a friend are going to a big exhibition. In your notebook, write the dialogue for one of the following situations.

1 You are speaking to the assistant at the ticket office – you and your friend both have student cards.
2 You are speaking to the assistant at one of the displays – you would like to take a photo using a flash.
3 You and your friend are saying goodbye to each other as you leave the exhibition.

The Grammar Builder

Welcome to the **Grammar Builder**!

- The Grammar Builder gives extensive and more detailed practice of the grammar points in the Snapshot course.

- The units in this section can be used alongside the units in the Workbook section, or for extra revision at a later stage.

- Each unit begins with a short grammar reference section called *Grammar highlights*. This gives further examples of the structures which are presented in the Students' Book. It also includes helpful additional notes.

- The practice exercises which follow the *Grammar highlights* are clearly labelled so that you know exactly which grammar point you are practising in each exercise.

Grammar highlights

Remember

Present simple for routines

I come here every year.
What do they do in their free time?
Do you like jazz?
Yes, I do. / No, I don't.
She doesn't usually teach at my school.
Does she work in London?
Yes, she does. / No, she doesn't.

- One use of the present simple is to talk about permanent situations and routines, e.g. *He works in a bank. She usually stays with me in the summer.*
- Adverbs of frequency come before the main verb, but after the verb *to be*, e.g. *He always arrives late. He is usually late.*
- Adverbial phrases of frequency come after the verb and the object, e.g. *We see her twice a week.*

Present continuous

I'm living in a hostel at the moment.
Who are you waiting for?
Is he working this week?
Yes, he is. / No, he isn't.
Why are they laughing?
They aren't laughing.

- One use of the present continuous is to talk about things which are happening at the time of speaking or in the current period, e.g. *He's lying in the sun at the moment. She's staying with her aunt this summer.*
- The following verbs are not normally used in the continuous form: *see, hear, notice, recognise, like, love, want, hate, know, mean, mind, believe, forget, remember.*

- It is not necessary to repeat the subject in a list of verbs in the present simple or present continuous, e.g. *He lives in Brighton, works in Lewes and goes to Bristol every weekend. I'm lying in the sun, drinking a milkshake and listening to the birds.*

Echo questions

She's visiting relatives at the moment.
Is she? I am, too.

She bought it last week.
Did she? It's lovely.

- We use echo questions to show interest or surprise.

Infinitive of purpose

Are you here to improve your English?
He isn't doing it to earn money; he's doing it to meet people.

- We can express a positive purpose by using an infinitive + *to*, e.g. *I'm doing exercises to get fit.*

Practice

● Present simple and present continuous

1 ⟩ Circle the correct answers and complete the sentences.

I always *eat* my breakfast at the bus stop.
(a) eat   b) am eating   c) eats

1 He *doesn't usually take* sugar in his coffee.
a) isn't usually taking   (b) doesn't usually take
c) usually isn't taking

2 *Are you listening* to this music or can I turn it off?
a) Do you listen   b) Does he listen
(c) Are you listening

3 *Do you know* any of the surfers in Newquay?
a) Are you knowing   b) You know
(c) Do you know

4 My sister *is staying* with a friend in California at the moment.
(a) is staying   b) stays   c) doesn't stay

5 He's ill so he *isn't working* today.
a) doesn't work   b) works   (c) isn't working

6 We sometimes *stay* in the youth hostel in Penzance.
a) staying   (b) stay   c) are staying

7 *Do they* always work at the pool on Saturday evenings?
(a) Do they   b) Are they   c) Is he

8 I'm busy at the moment. I *'m making* a cake for Eddie's birthday.
a) make   (b) 'm making   c) do making

● Present simple and present continuous

2 ⟩ Use the prompts to write sentences in the present simple or the present continuous.

Andrea's in the garden. She (help) Mark with the barbecue.

Andrea's in the garden. She's helping Mark with the barbecue.

1 Can I turn the tape off? I (not like) this music.
Can I turn the tape off? I don't like this music

2 Please be quiet! I (do) my Maths homework.
Please be quiet. I'm doing my Maths homework

3 Claudia and David (stay) with us at the moment.
Claudia and D. staying with us at the moment

4 What time (you usually / start) work?
What time do you usually start work?

5 Listen to this Stevie Wonder tape. He (have got) a great voice.
Luisa is having her guitar lesson at the moment. She has one every Tuesday

6 Luisa (have) her guitar lesson at the moment. She (have) one every Tuesday.
Listen to this Stevie Wonder tape. He has a great voice.

7 My CD player (need) new batteries.
My CD player needs new batteries

8 It (not rain) very much in summer in North Africa.
It doesn't rain very much in summer in North Africa

Practice

● **Present simple and present continuous**

3 > Complete the letter, putting the verbs in brackets into the present simple or present continuous.

Dear Tara,
I **'m having** (have) a fantastic time
in Florida. I ¹ _'m staying_ (stay) with
my aunt and uncle and two cousins.
I ² _have got_ (have got) a long list
of books to read before next term, but
I ³ _haven't read_ (not read) any of them!
In fact I ⁴ _'m not using_ (not use) my
brain at all! Instead I ⁵ _'m getting_ (get)
a tan and I ⁶ _'m studying_ (study) the art
of total relaxation!
Right now I ⁷ _'m sitting_ (sit) in the
garden with my feet in the swimming pool.
I ⁸ _'m drinking_ (drink) a big chocolate
milkshake. The sun ⁹ _is shining_ (shine)
and the birds ¹⁰ _singing_ (sing).
Every day we ¹¹ _go_ (go) to
the beach. I ¹² _'m learning_ (learn) to
water ski. I'm not very good yet and I often
¹³ _fall_ (fall) over but it's fun.
Sometimes I ¹⁴ _borrow_ (borrow) my
cousins' jet-ski. It's brilliant fun but the

jet-ski ¹⁵ _makes_ (make) a terrible
noise. I'm afraid the people on the beach
¹⁶ _don't like_ (not like) it.
The food here is great. I ¹⁷ _'m getting_ (get)
fat because it's so delicious. I usually
¹⁸ _have_ (have) a milkshake and ice cream
for breakfast! We ¹⁹ _don't eat_ (not eat)
a big lunch – usually just sandwiches and fruit
salad. In the evenings my uncle always
²⁰ _has_ (have) a barbecue.
I ²¹ _love_ (love) the hamburgers
and sausages here.
²² _Are you having_ (you/have) a nice time
in Cambridge? Is your job at Patsy's Pizzas
OK? What time ²³ _do you start_ (you/start)
work every day? ²⁴ _do you get_ (you/get)
a free lunch at the restaurant?
²⁵ _Is Martin working_ (Martin/work)
hard for his exams?
    Write soon and tell me all your news.
        Love,
        Phil

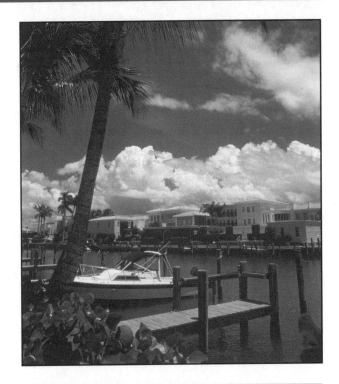

● **Echo questions**

4 > Write responses using echo questions.

Ted: I live in the centre of New York.
Gill: **Do you**? I live in a small village in
Scotland.

1 Pete: I've got three brothers and a sister.
Joy: _Have you_......? I'm an only child.

2 Kim: This pizza's horrible.
Ron: _Is it_......? Mine's delicious.

3 May: Sandra's playing tennis at the sports centre.
Lin: _Is she_......? Who's she playing with?

4 Vic: Alan's got a job as a lifeguard.
Neil: _Has he_......? How much is he earning?
(Does)

5 Tina: I'm competing in a water-ski championship.
Bill: _Are you_......? When?

6 Pat: My parents are learning to dance the tango.
Jon: _Are they_......? That's really funny.

7 Bob: Andy loves his part-time job.
Jen: _Does he_......? How much does he earn?

8 Gail: Liza and Nick have got tickets for the
Robbie Williams concert.
Mike: _Have they_......? I don't like Robbie Williams.

9 Ann: I usually cycle to college.
Lee: _Do you_......? I go by bus.

87

Practice

● Infinitive of purpose

5▷ Complete the prompts by matching the activities in the box with the people and places. Then write sentences using the present continuous of *go* with an infinitive of purpose.

- buy some tennis balls
- pay for the tickets
- (change some money)
- get some aspirins
- have a drink
- meet your friend
- play badminton
- get some stamps

(Dave / bank / *change some money* ?)
Is Dave going to the bank to change some money?

1 (Sandy and Alice / travel agent's / *pay for the tickets* ?)
Are S. and A. going to the travel agent's to pay for the tickets?

2 (you / station / *meet your friend* ?)
Are you going to the station to meet your friend?

3 (Melissa / chemist's / *get some aspirins* ?)
Is Melissa going to chemist's to get some aspirins?

4 (we / café / *have a drink* ?)
Are we going to the café to have a drink?

5 (Adrian / sports shop / *buy some tennis balls* ?)
Is Adrian going to the sports shop to buy some tennis balls?

6 (Lola / post office / *get some stamps* ?)
Is Lola going to the post office to get some stamps?

7 (they / sports centre / *play badminton* ?)
Are they going to the sports centre to play badminton?

● Infinitive of purpose

6▷ Match the sentence halves and write the complete sentences.

Does he cycle to work — `e`
1 We're going to the sports centre — `B`
2 They usually work in the summer holidays — `A`
3 He goes to dance classes — `D`
4 She's meeting the manager — `G`
5 I'm phoning — `C`
6 Are you going to France — `F`

a) to earn some extra money.
b) to have a swim.
c) to invite you to my party.
d) to meet girls.
e) to save money?
f) to study French?
g) to talk about her new job.

Does he cycle to work to save money?

1 *We're going to the sports centre to have a swim.*
2 *They usually work in the summer holidays to earn some extra money.*
3 *He goes to dance classes to meet girls.*
4 *She's meeting the manager to talk about her new job.*
5 *I'm phoning to invite you to my party.*
6 *Are you going to France to study French?*

Unit 2

Grammar highlights

Past simple

We arrived late.
She left early.
They didn't stay.
Did you meet your friend?
Yes, I did. / No, I didn't.
Who did you talk to?
Didn't you meet anyone?
They arrived last week.
I met her this summer.
Didn't she phone this morning?

- The past simple positive form of regular verbs ends in *-ed*. In most cases, we add *ed* to the infinitive: *climb/climbed*, *but*:
  — if the infinitive ends in e, we add *d*: *arrive/arrived; die/died*.
  — if the infinitive ends in a consonant + y, we delete the ~~y~~ and add *ied*: *study/studied; cry/cried*.
  — if the infinitive ends in a stressed syllable of one vowel and one consonant (not *y* or *w*), we double the consonant: *trip/tripped; step/stepped*.
  Note: There are some exceptions, e.g. *travel/travelled*.
- There is a list of irregular verbs at the back of this book.

- We make questions with *did* + infinitive and negative statements with *didn't* + infinitive.

- We often use time adverbials with the past simple, e.g. *I arrived an hour ago*.
- We say *in the morning/afternoon/ evening* but *at night*.
- We do not use prepositions in time adverbials if we are using the demonstrative pronoun *this*, e.g. *They arrived this morning.* (**not** ~~They arrived in this morning~~.)

Conjunctions *so* and *because*

I was tired so I went to bed.
I went to bed because I was tired.

- We use *so* to talk about a consequence and *because* to talk about a reason.

Linkers: *first (of all), then, before (breakfast), after (that), later, the next day, in the end*

Practice

● Past simple: positive forms

1 > Complete the passage, putting the verbs in brackets in the past simple.

My trip to the United States _**started**_ (start) badly for me. I [1] _had_ (have) a lot to do so I [2] _got_ (get) up very early. First I [3] _went_ (go) to the travel agent's to collect my ticket. Then I [4] _got_ (get) some American dollars from the bank. After that I [5] _took_ (take) my two goldfish to my neighbour's house and [6] _leaved_ (leave) them there for the week.

Suddenly I [7] _rememberd_ (remember) my library books, and I [8] _ran_ (run) to the library and [9] _gave_ (give) them back. On the way back from the library I [10] _stoped_ (stop) at the shops and [11] _bought_ (buy) some sunglasses and films for my camera.

I [12] _came_ (come) home, [13] _ate_ (eat) a sandwich and [14] _made_ (make) myself some coffee. Finally, I [15] _packed_ (pack) my bags, [16] _walked_ (walk) out of the door and [17] _caught_ (catch) the bus to the airport. At the airport, I [18] _found_ (find) the right check-in desk and [19] _showed_ (show) the man my ticket. He [20] _shook_ (shake) his head and [21] _said_ (say) 'I'm afraid you're a day early. This ticket is for July 12th. It's July 11th today.'

● Past simple: all forms

2 > Write questions and answers in the past simple.

Q: Why you (miss) the bus?
A: Because I (not hear) my alarm clock.
Q: _**Why did you miss the bus?**_
A: _**Because I didn't hear my alarm clock.**_

1 Q: you (find) your swimming costume?
A: No, so I (not go) swimming.
Q: _Did you find your swimming costume?_
A: _No, so I didnt go swimming._

2 Q: How long the journey (take)?
A: It (not take) very long. About an hour.
Q: _How long the journey took?_
A: _It didnt take very long. About an hour_

3 Q: What they (do) in Amsterdam?
A: They (not go) in the end. They (miss) the plane!
Q: _What they did in Amsterdam?_
A: _They didn't go in the end. They missed the plane!_

4 Q: Where she (buy) her purple jeans?
A: She (not buy) them. I (give) them to her.
Q: _Where she bought her purple jeans?_
A: _She didn't buy them. I gave them to her._

5 Q: your sister (lose) her passport?
A: No, she (not lose) her passport. She (lose) her plane ticket.
Q: _Did your sister lose her passport?_
A: _No, she didnt lose her passport. She lost her plane ticket._

Practice

- Past simple
- Linkers

- Past simple
- Conjunction *because*

3 > Complete the passage, putting the verbs in brackets in the past simple and filling in the blanks a) to d) with the linkers in the box.

- Then   - Later   - (First of all)   - After
- The next day

Last year we **spent** (spend) two weeks camping on St Agnes, one of the Scilly Isles, off the coast of Cornwall. It ¹ _was_ (be) a very long and tiring journey to get there. **First of all** we ² _took_ (take) a taxi to Paddington station at five in the morning.
a) _Then_ we ³ _caught_ (catch) the train to Penzance, in Cornwall. b) _Later_ that we ⁴ _walked_ (walk) from Penzance station to the docks. At Penzance docks we ⁵ _got_ (get) a ferry to an island called St Mary's. Unfortunately, the sea ⁶ _was_ (be) very rough and we ⁷ _were_ (be) all sick on the ferry. When we ⁸ _arrived_ (arrive) at St Mary's, we ⁹ _went_ (go) to a café to relax.
c) _The next day_, when we ¹⁰ _felt_ (feel) better, we ¹¹ _took_ (take) a small boat to St Agnes. The campsite owner ¹² _met_ (meet) us at St Agnes quay and ¹³ _gave_ (give) us a lift to the campsite on his tractor. We ¹⁴ _put_ (put) up our tents and ¹⁵ _went_ (go) to bed early. d) _After_ we ¹⁶ _slept_ (sleep) really late.

4 > Match the sentence halves. Then write the sentences in the past simple with *because*.

The neighbours (complain) about the party   **b**

1 He (sleep) late this morning   E
2 They (run) to the station   H
3 He (wake) up suddenly   G
4 She (not enjoy) the party   F
5 We (have) a terrible holiday   C
6 She (wear) three sweaters   D
7 I (not phone) him   A

a) I (not have) his phone number.
b) (the music (be) too loud.)
c) it (rain) every day.
d) she (feel) very cold.
e) he (not go) to bed until after midnight.
f) she (not know) anyone.
g) there (be) a loud noise in the night.
h) they (not want) to miss the train.

The neighbours complained about the party because the music was too loud.

1 He slept late this morning because he didn't go to bed until after midnight.
2 They ran to the station because they didn't want to miss the train.
3 She didn't enjoyed the party because she didn't know anyone.
4 He woke up suddenly because there was a loud noise in the night.
5 We had a terrible holiday because it rained every day.
6 She wore three sweaters because she felt very cold.
7 I didn't phone him because I didn't have his phone number.

Practice

- Past simple
- Conjunction *so*

- Past simple
- Conjunctions *so* and *because*

5 > Rewrite the sentences in Exercise 4 using *so*.

The music was too loud so the neighbours complained about the party.

1 He didn't go to bed until after midnight so he slept late this morning.

2 They didn't want to miss the train so they ran to the station.

3 There was a loud noise in the night so he woke up suddenly.

4 She didn't know anyone so she didn't enjoyed the party.

5 It rained every day so we had a terrible holiday.

6 She felt very cold so she wore three sweaters.

7 I didn't have his phone number so I didn't phone him.

6 > Write sentences with *so* or *because* putting the verbs in brackets in the past simple.

She (not go) surfing; the weather (be) terrible.
She didn't go surfing because the weather was terrible.

I (can't) find my tennis racket; I (borrow) yours.
I couldn't find my tennis racket so I borrowed yours.

1 They (miss) the bus; they (take) a taxi.
They missed the bus so they took a taxi.

2 We (lose) our tickets; we (can't) go to the match.
We lost our tickets because we couldn't go to the match.

3 The film (annoy) me; nothing (happen) in it.
They film annoyed me because nothing happened in it.

4 They (complain); they (not like) the food.
They complained because they didn't like the food.

5 My aunt (give) me some money; I (buy) some tapes.
My aunt gave me some money so I bought some tapes.

6 He (borrow) my mobile phone; he (want) to phone his girlfriend.
He borrowed my mobile phone because he wanted to phone his girlfriend.

Grammar highlights

Remember

Defining relative clauses with *who, which, where*

The girl who lives next door is Australian.
Where is the money which was on the table?
I know a place where you can get cheap CDs.

- Defining relative clauses give essential information. They do not have commas.

Non-defining relative clauses with *who, which, where*

Jim, who loves cooking, made that cake.
Strawberries, which are my favourite fruit, are delicious with sugar and fresh cream.
I often go to stay in Penzance, which is a busy seaside town in Cornwall.
Penzance, where my friend Georgia lives, is a busy seaside town.

- Non-defining relative clauses, which give extra information and which can be left out, have a comma before the relative clause and a comma or full stop after it.

- In relative clauses, we use *who* to refer to people, *which* to refer to things and *where* to refer to places.
- In defining relative clauses, we can also use *that* to refer to people and things, *e.g. He's got a jacket that cost £200.*

Future with *going to*

I'm going to walk.
We aren't going to take the bus.
Are you going to buy a new bike?
Yes, I am. / No, I'm not.
Isn't Lucy going to give us a lift?

- We use *going to* to talk about intentions, e.g. *'There's no milk.' 'Yes, I know. I'm going to buy some.'*
- We also use *going to* for predictions about the immediate future, particularly when we already have evidence of what is going to happen, e.g. *Look at those clouds. It's going to rain.*

Future with *will/won't*

I'll (will) be back soon. (promise)
Jim won't (will not) be late. (prediction)
You'll (will) be sorry. (threat)
OK, we'll (will) leave tomorrow. (decision)
Will there be a night bus?
Yes, there will. / No, there won't.
Won't it be dangerous to cycle in the dark?

- We use *will/won't* for predictions, promises, threats and decisions. We also use *will/won't* to give opinions after verbs like *be sure, think, know* and *hope.*

Future with present continuous

We're seeing him tomorrow.
They aren't coming on Sunday.
Are you working next week?
Yes, I am. / No, I'm not.
Aren't they getting married this July?

- We use the present continuous to talk about definite future arrangements. This tense is common with time phrases, e.g. *I'm seeing Jim tomorrow.*

Practice

● Relative clauses

1 ⟩ Complete the sentences with *who, which* or *where*. **Add commas where necessary.**

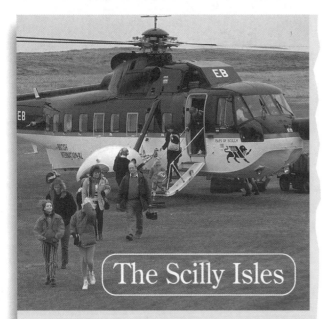

The Scilly Isles

You can go to the Scilly Isles ..., **which** are off the coast of Cornwall ..., by ferry, helicopter or plane.

1 There are about 300 islands but there are only six ...*which*... have people on them.

2 The Scillies ...*which*... are also called the Scilly Isles have a mild climate.

3 St Mary's is the island ...*where*... the ferry and helicopter arrive from Penzance.

4 Tresco ...*which*... is one of the biggest islands is famous for its tropical gardens.

5 People ...*who*... like wildlife will love seeing the birds and seals on Annet.

6 On St Mary's there are places ...*where*... you can ride horses.

7 Pelistry Bay .... you can sometimes swim with seals is a beautiful sandy beach on St Mary's.

8 Michael Morpurgo .... writes books for children lived on the Scillies for a long time.

● Future with present continuous

2 ⟩ Read Claudia's diary for next week. Write about her week using the present continuous.

Sunday 19 July	(morning) go swimming with Mark
Monday 20 July	buy birthday present for Nadia
Tuesday 21 July	(evening) go to Nadia's party with Luisa
Wednesday 22 July	meet Cathy for lunch
Thursday 23 July	play tennis with Luisa
Friday 24 July	Anita and Frankie arrive
Saturday 25 July	go to Oasis concert with Anita and Frankie

On Sunday morning she **'s going swimming with Mark.**

1 On Monday Claudia ....
....

2 On Tuesday evening Claudia and Luisa ....
....

3 On Wednesday she ....
....

4 On Thursday she ....
....

5 On Friday Anita and Frankie ....
....

6 On Saturday Claudia ....
....

Practice

● **Future with** *'ll (will)/won't*

3 ⟩ **Write questions and answers, using the verbs in brackets with** *'ll (will)/won't.*

Q: When (you / phone) me?
A: I (phone) tomorrow. I (not forget)

Q: *When will you phone me?*

A: *I'll phone tomorrow. I won't forget.*

1 Q: What time (you / get) back?
   A: We (be) back by midnight. We (not be) late.
   Q: *What time are you going get back?*
   A: *We'll be back by midnight, so We won't be late.*

2 Q: How (they / get) home from the club?
   A: There (not be) any buses so they (have) to get a taxi.
   Q: *How will they get home*
   A: *There won't be any buses so they'll have to get a taxi.*

3 Q: (you / write) to me soon?
   A: I (not write) but I (phone) you from Paris.
   Q: *Will you write to me soon.*
   A: *I won't write but I'll phone you from Paris.*

4 Q: (you / have) a drink?
   A: I (not have) a drink, thanks. I (have) a sandwich.
   Q: *Will you have a drink?*
   A: *I won't have a drink, thanks. I'll have a sandwich.*

5 Q: What (the weather / be) like?
   A: It (not be) hot. It (rain), I think.
   Q: *What will the weather be like?*
   A: *I won't be hot. It will rain, I think.*

● **Future with present continuous**
● **Future with** *'ll (will)/won't*

4 ⟩ **Write sentences, putting the verbs in brackets in the present continuous or the future with** *'ll/won't.*

That box looks heavy. I (help) you with it.

That box looks heavy. I'll help you with it.

1 Don't forget. You (see) the doctor at four o'clock tomorrow.
   Don't forget. You are seeing the doctor at four o'clock tomorrow.

2 Anna and Sam (have) a beach party on Saturday.
   Anna and Sam are going to have a beach party on Saturday.

3 I know I (forget) everything in the exam and I (not write) anything.
   I know I'll forget anything in the exam and I won't write anything

4 '(you / do) anything tonight?' 'Yes. We (go) to a concert at the Albert Hall.'
   Are you doing anything tonight? Yes. We are going to a concert at the Albert Hall.

5 'Where (you / wait) for me?' 'I (meet) you outside the cinema at six.'
   Where will you wait for me? I'll meet you outside the cinema at six

6 You can tell Martin your secret. He (not repeat) it.
   He won't repeat it.

7 He can't come tomorrow. He (go) to Bristol.
   He is going to Bristol.

3

Practice

● **Future with** *going to*

● **Future with present continuous**

● **Future with** *will/won't*

● **Future with** *going to*

5 Complete the conversation, putting the verbs in brackets in the present continuous if possible. If it is not possible, use *going to*.

Tony: Let's go to the beach on Saturday.

Steve: I can't. **I'm looking** (I / look) after my little brother, Tim. My parents ¹ *are going* (go) to Bristol tomorrow and ² *They're leaving* (they / leave) him at home with me.

Tony: How long ³ *are they going being* (they / be) in Bristol?

Steve: ⁴ *They're staying* (they / stay) there a week. I don't think ⁵ *I'm having* (I / have) a very nice time with Tim. I looked after him last year and he was very naughty. This year ⁶ *I'm trying* (I / try) to be very strict right from the start! ⁷ *Are you doing* (you / do) anything tonight?

Tony: ⁸ *I'm going* (I / go) to Alex's party. But I'm a bit worried because I've got my driving test tomorrow morning and ⁹ *I'm going to be* (I / be) really tired.

6 Complete the sentences, using the verbs in brackets with *'ll (will)/won't* **or** *going to*.

I'm not going to the cinema with them. I know **I won't like** (I / not like) the film.

1 'What are you doing with my camera?'
'...... *I'm going to take* ...... (I / take) a photo of Nina on her new motorbike.'

2 I'm not going to the party because ...... *I won't know* ...... (I / not know) anybody.

3 Have a nice weekend. ...... *I'll see* ...... (I / see) you on Monday.

4 I'm really happy. *Anthony and Heidi* *A getting* (Anthony and Heidi / get) married.

5 Dave's wearing his white shorts. ...... *He is going to play* ...... (He / play) tennis.

6 'I haven't got any money.'
'Really? ...... *I'll lend* ...... (I / lend) you some.'

7 'What are you doing with the shampoo?'
'...... *I'm going to wash* ...... (I / wash) the dog.'

8 'What would you like to eat?'
'...... *I won't have* ...... (I / not have) anything, thank you.'

9 'Why is Diane getting into the car?'
'...... *She is going to take* ...... (She / take) Ruth to the station.'

I'm going to have

going to try

Unit 4

Grammar highlights

Present perfect simple with *for* and *since*

She's been here for an hour.
She's been here since one o'clock.
Have you worked here for a long time?
Yes, I have. / No, I haven't.
How long have you known Jim?
I've known him for two months.
I've known him since July.
I haven't seen him for a week.

● One use of the present perfect simple is to talk about events which started in the past and have a result now, e.g. *I've known Sue for two years.* (= I met Sue two years ago. I still know her.)

● When we use the present perfect simple tense, we use *for* to talk about a period of time, e.g *three hours*, and *since* to talk about a point in time, e.g *last Wednesday*.

Comparison of adjectives

Short adjectives

strong	stronger	strongest
fit	fitter	fittest
happy	happier	happiest

Long adjectives

important	more important	most important

Irregular adjectives

good	better	best
bad	worse	worst
far	further	furthest

Comparative
The beach is more crowded today than yesterday.
It's usually hotter in August than in July.

Superlative
She's one of the best surfers in Cornwall.
It's the most exciting sport I've ever done.

● We form the comparative of short adjectives (not ending in *y*) by adding *er* or *r*, and the superlative by adding *est* or *st*, e.g. *strong, stronger, strongest; large, larger, largest.*

● When an adjective has one or two syllables and ends in *y*, we usually form the comparative and superlative by deleting the *y* and adding *ier/iest*, e.g. *funny, funnier, funniest.*

● When an adjective has one syllable and ends in one vowel and one consonant, we double the final consonant in the comparative and superlative, e.g. *fit, fitter, fittest.*

● To form the comparative and superlative of long adjectives, we put *more* or *most* in front of the adjective, e.g. *more independent, most independent.*

Intensifier *much* + comparative adjective

He's much healthier than his brother.

● We can use the intensifier *much* to make a comparative stronger.

Comparison with *(not) as ... as*

This CD isn't as good as her first one.
My bike was just as expensive as yours.
Is the water as cold as it was yesterday?

● We can also use *as ... as* with *almost, nearly* or *just*, e.g. *The beach is almost as crowded as it was yesterday.*

Practice

● **Present perfect simple with** *for* **and** *since*

1 › Use the prompts to write questions in the present perfect and answers with *for* or *since*.

Q: you / live / in California?
A: seven months

Q: *How long have you lived in California?*

A: *I've lived in California for seven months.*

1 **Q:** they / know / each other?
A: January

Q: ....

A: ....

2 **Q:** she / have / a motorbike?
A: two years

Q: ....

A: ....

....

3 **Q:** he / work / at the Funk Club?
A: last year

Q: ....

A: ....

....

4 **Q:** she / be / at the beach?
A: about an hour

Q: ....

A: ....

....

5 **Q:** they / live / in Canada?
A: years and years

Q: ....

A: ....

....

6 **Q:** you / be / here?
A: July 3rd

Q: ....

A: ....

....

● **Present perfect simple with** *for* **and** *since*

2 › Complete the letter, putting the verbs in brackets in the present perfect and filling in blanks a) to h) with *for* or *since*.

Dear Alex,

I'm sorry I __haven't written__ (not write)
__for__ weeks and weeks.
I 1 _has been_ (be) very busy
a) _since_ I started college.
 b) _Since_ the beginning of
term, I 2 _has read_ (read) seven
books on the Russian Revolution and
I 3 _has done_ (do) three History
essays. Life is just work, work, work.
I 4 _hasn't seen_ (not see) a good
film c) _for_ about a month,
I 5 _hasn't played_ (not play) tennis
d) _for_ about two months and
I 6 _hasn't met_ (not meet) any new

people e) _Since_ January. I am
living a very unhealthy life. And another
thing — I 7 _hasn't slept_ (not sleep)
very well f) _for_ a very long time.
I'm seeing the college doctor about
that tomorrow.
 8 _Has you seen_ (you/see) Martha
g) _Since_ your birthday party?
I 9 _hasn't had_ (not have) a letter
from her h) _for_ a very long time.
If you see her, give her my love.
I hope you like the photos of your
party.
     Write soon.
          Love,
               Jessica

Practice

● Comparative and superlative adjectives

3 > Look at the club guide. Write a comparative and a superlative sentence for each adjective.

YOUR GUIDE TO THE BEST CLUBS

	Dr Funk	The Garage	Secrets
Crowded	★★★	★★	★
1 Expensive	★	★★	★★★
2 Lively	★★★	★★	★
3 Noisy	★★★	★★	★
4 Good music	★★★	★★	★
5 Interesting people	★★	★	★★★

The Garage is more crowded than Secrets.

Dr Funk is the most crowded.

1 The Garage *is less expensive than S*

more than F

Secrets *is the most expensive*

2 The Garage *is more lively than S*

Dr Funk *is the most lively*

3 The Garage *is more noisy than S*

Dr Funk *is the most noisy*

4 The Garage has *much good music than S*

Dr Funk has *the best music*

5 Dr Funk has *interesting people than G*

Secrets has *the most interesting people*

● Intensifier *much/a bit* + comparative adjective
● Comparison with *just as/not as … as*

4 > Use the prompts to make comparisons with *much/a bit* + comparative adjective or *just as/not as* + adjective.

today (38°C) / yesterday (28°C) (hot)

Today's much hotter than yesterday.

today (33°C) / yesterday (32°C) (hot)

Today's a bit hotter than yesterday.

today (30°C) / yesterday (30°C) (hot)

Today's just as hot as yesterday.

today (27°C) / yesterday (31°C) (hot)

Today's not as hot as yesterday.

1 Racehorses (72 km per hour) / cheetahs (69 km per hour) / (fast)

R is a bit faster than ch.

2 Michael Jordan (£25 million per year) / the football player David Beckham (£9 million) (well-paid)

J. is much well-paid than B

3 Sumatran rhinos (about 200 left) / giant pandas (about 200 left) (endangered)

S is just as endangered as giant

4 Andrea (1m 70) / Serena (1m 75) (tall)

A. isnt as tall as S

5 Blue whales (120 tonnes) / elephants (5.2 tonnes) (heavy)

B w is much more heavy than e

6 A Zeta watch (£35) / a Romeo watch (£33) (expensive)

A Z. is a bit expensive than R

7 The River Amazon (6,400 km) / the River Nile (6,600 km) (short)

R.A is a bit short than R N.

Unit 6

Grammar highlights

Past simple and past continuous with time markers *while, as, when*

While I was swimming, somebody stole my clothes.
I was watching TV when I heard a scream.
As we were talking, the lights went out.
He wasn't going fast when his car hit the tree.
What was she wearing when you saw her?
Was she wearing a hat when you saw her?

- We often use the past simple and the past continuous tense in the same sentence. The past continuous describes the longer action or situation and the past simple describes the shorter action or situation, e.g. *While I was talking to Jane, Rob ran past.*

- Clauses in the past continuous are often introduced by *while* and *as*. Clauses in the past simple are often introduced by *when*.

- When the *while*, *when* or *as* clause comes first, it is followed by a comma.

Prepositions of motion: *across, along, from, towards, through, past, into, over, under, up, down*

Practice

● Past continuous or past simple

1 > Put the verbs in brackets in the past continuous or past simple.

She (wait) to pay for her shopping when somebody (steal) her purse.

She was waiting to pay for her shopping when somebody stole her purse.

1 How fast (he / drive) when he (hit) the other car?

....

....

2 The phone (ring) while we (watch) a programme about surfing.

....

....

3 As she (get) ready to dive, somebody (push) her in.

....

....

4 I (not go) very fast when I (fall) off my motorbike.

....

....

5 When you (pull) her out of the water, (she / breathe)?

....

....

6 (you / live) in Spain when you (meet) your girlfriend?

....

....

7 As they (leave) the beach, they suddenly (hear) a scream.

....

....

8 She (drown) when he suddenly (see) her and (rescue) her.

....

....

9 He (take) my bag while I (not look).

....

....

● Past continuous or past simple

2 > Complete the passage, putting the verbs in the correct tense: past simple or past continuous.

Last weekend my brother **_invited_** (invite) three friends to our house. Since they **_were playing_** (play) a very noisy game, I ¹........................ (decide) to do my homework in the park. I ²........................ (find) a quiet bench in the park and sat down. I ³........................ (write) the first sentence of my English essay when an old lady ⁴........................ (sit) down next to me. She ⁵........................ (open) a plastic bag and ⁶........................ (start) to throw bread on the ground. Suddenly there were about thirty birds around us. They ⁷........................ (make) a terrible noise so I stopped writing and ⁸........................ (put) my notebook and pen down on the ground. I ⁹........................ (watch) the birds and ¹⁰........................ (think) about my English essay when a boy ¹¹........................ (skate) past very fast. He skated over my pen and ¹²........................ (break) it. I ¹³........................ (not have) another pen so I ¹⁴........................ (have) to go home to write my essay.

Practice

● Past simple   ● Prepositions of motion

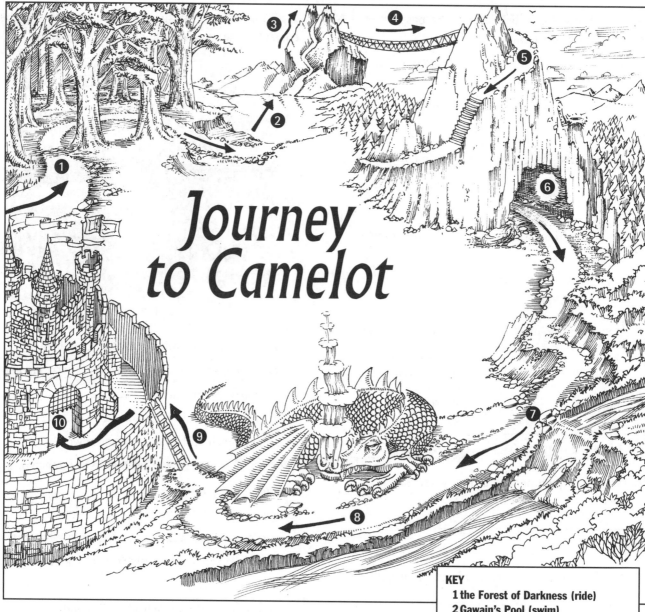

KEY
1 the Forest of Darkness (ride)
2 Gawain's Pool (swim)
3 Mount Misery (climb)
4 Tristan's Bridge (walk)
5 Mount Joy (walk)
6 the Tunnel of Understanding (run)
7 the Golden River (walk)
8 the sleeping dragon (tiptoe)
9 the wall (climb)
10 Camelot Castle (go)

3 ⟩ Write sentences about the game, using the past simple of the verbs in brackets and a preposition from the box.

- across - along - down - into - past
- over - over (- through) - through - up

1   *We rode through the Forest of Darkness.*

2 ....

3 ....

4 ....

5 ....

6 ....

7 ....

8 ....

9 ....

10 ....

102

Grammar highlights

Remember

Question tags

Positive statements with negative tags

We're in trouble, aren't we?

He's got a bike, hasn't he?

She knows Rosie, doesn't she?

I told you, didn't I?

I haven't failed my exam, have I?

She can speak Chinese, can't she?

It'll be sunny tomorrow, won't it?

Negative statements with positive tags

We aren't late, are we?

They haven't got a car, have they?

They don't eat meat, do they?

You didn't find her, did you?

She hasn't seen us, has she?

He can't dive, can he?

You won't lose the money, will you?

Present perfect simple with time adverbials *just, already, yet*

I've just seen a brilliant film.

They've already told me about it.

Mark hasn't arrived yet.

Have you spoken to Angela yet?

He's already seen *Titanic*. He saw it last month.

He's just bought a motorbike. He bought it in Brighton.

I got my new camera last week but I haven't used it yet.

Past simple and present perfect simple

Laura's just got back from California. She went there two weeks ago for her cousin's wedding.

- One use of question tags is to check information.

- We use a positive statement followed by a negative tag when we expect the answer *Yes*, e.g. *You're American, aren't you?*

- We use a negative statement followed by a positive tag when we expect the answer *No*, e.g. *They haven't arrived yet, have they?*

- The present perfect simple tense is often used with the words *just, already* and *yet*. The words *just* and *already* come between the auxiliary verb *have* and the main verb. The word *yet* comes at the end of the sentence.

- We normally use *just* and *already* in positive statements.

- We normally use *yet* in questions and negative statements.

- We use the present perfect simple tense to talk about an action in the past that has a result now. We use the past simple tense to talk about a completed action in the past.

- With past time adverbials like *ago, yesterday, last year, in 1989*, we use the past simple (not the present perfect simple) e.g. *I saw him a week ago.* (**not** *I've seen him a week ago.*)

- The verb *go* has two present perfect forms: *have/has gone* and *have/has been*. We use *have/has been* when the person has made a visit and come back, e.g. *She has been to Newquay* (= She has visited Newquay and returned.) We use *have/has gone* when the person has not returned, e.g. *He has gone to India.* (= He is in India. He isn't here.)

Practice

● **Question tags: positive statement, negative tag**

1 **Complete the questions with the correct tags.**

You know Carlo, **don't you?**

1 We've met before, *haven't we?*

2 You were at the party, *weren't you?*

3 She can stay here, *can't she?*

4 I was in a bad mood, *wasn't you?*

5 We'll see you tomorrow, *won't we?*

6 You've been to California, *haven't you?*

7 They work at the pool, *don't they?*

8 We're in the wrong place, *aren't we?*

9 I gave her the money, *didn't you?*

10 You're the new lifeguard, *aren't you?*

11 I look good in blue, *don't you?*

12 Your brother's a surfer, *isn't he?*

● **Question tags: negative statement, positive tag**

2 **Complete the questions with the correct tags.**

You haven't seen Judy, **have you?**

1 The sun's not very hot today, *is it?*

2 They can't swim very well, *can they?*

3 You didn't mind, *did you?*

4 Ruth doesn't eat meat, *does she?*

5 She isn't a vegetarian, *is she?*

6 Philip won't tell anyone, *will he?*

7 He hasn't got a motorbike, *has he?*

8 The water wasn't very cold, *was it?*

9 We aren't going to Darren's house, *are we?*

10 You haven't been to Alaska, *have you?*

11 The sandwiches weren't very good, *were they?*

12 You don't smile very often, *do you?*

13 I'm not very tall, *am I?*

14 We haven't made any mistakes, *have we?*

Let's go to the cinema, shall we.

● **Question tags: positive and negative**

3 **Match the sentence halves. Then write the sentences and add question tags.**

Francine isn't   **b**

1 Neil Armstrong was   *h*

2 Shakespeare wrote   *g*

3 There aren't any   *c*

4 Leonardo DiCaprio doesn't wear   *e*

5 This book has got   *a*

6 The Romans didn't stay   *f*

7 The Beatles were   *d*

a) 144 pages.

b) an Italian name.

c) bears in Scotland.

d) big in the sixties.

e) glasses.

f) long in Britain.

g) *Romeo and Juliet.*

h) the first person on the moon.

Francine isn't an Italian name, is it?

1   *h*   *wasn't he*

2   *didn't he*

3   *are there*

4   *does he*

5   *hasn't it*

6   *did it*

7   *weren't they?*

Practice

● **Present perfect simple with** *yet*

4 Use the prompts to write pairs of sentences.
Use the present perfect simple + *yet* and the
present continuous + *still*.

Marisa (not iron) her shirt; she (have) a bath.

Marisa hasn't ironed her shirt yet; she's still
having a bath.

1 Paul (not get up); he (read) in bed.

P hasn't got up yet.
He's still reading in bed

2 'Tom (pass) his driving test?' 'No, he (have) driving
lessons.'

Has T passed his d. test yet?
No, he still not having d. lessons

3 Martha (look) for her keys; she (not find) them.

M. is still looking for her keys
she's not found them yet

4 '(you / buy) a surfboard?' 'No, I (save) up for one.'

Have you bought a s yet?
No, I'm still saving
up for one.

5 She (cut) her hair; she (not wash) it.

She's still cutting
her hair. She hasn't
washed it yet

6 Ben (eat) his lunch; he (not finish) his ice cream.

B. is still eating his lunch
He's not finished his
ice cream yet

7 '(you / buy) a new watch?' 'No, I (use) my
grandfather's watch.'

Have you bought a new watch
yet? No, I'm still
using my g. watch

105

Practice

● **Present perfect simple with time adverbials** *just, already, yet*

5 > **Complete the letter. Put the verbs in the present perfect simple and write the correct time phrase if given.**

Dear Michael,

Thank you very much for the card and flowers which **have just arrived** ([*just/yet*] arrive). I 1 **'ve been** (be) in hospital for ten days now but I 2 **'ve not had** (not have) time to get bored 3 **yet** [*already/yet*]. Most of my friends 4 **have visited** (visit) me every day. In fact Laura 5 **has just left** ([*just/yet*] leave). Lisa 6 **hasn't come yet** ([*already/yet*] not come) but it's hard for her as she's working AND studying at the moment. Since I 7 **'ve been** (be) here, I 8 **'ve already read** ([*just/already*] read) three books – long ones – and I 9 **'ve written** (write) about sixteen letters.

Somebody 10 **has just turned on** ([*just/yet*] turn on) the TV. There's an excellent comedy channel

on it and there's a Mr Bean film on at the moment. I 11 **'ve already seen** ([*just/already*] see) it and I don't want to see it again, so I'll continue with this letter.

12 **Have you bought** (you/buy) a new windsurfer 13 **yet** [*just/yet*]? 14 **Has Mr J. given** (Mr Jackson/give) you back the History projects? 15 **Has your b. gone** (your brother/go) to South America 16 **yet** [*just/yet*]? 17 **Has T. invited** (Tom/invite) Maria out 18 **yet** [*just/yet*]?

Write soon and tell me all the news.

Lots of love,

Rebecca

● **Past simple and present perfect simple**

6 > **Put the verbs in brackets in the past simple or the present perfect simple.**

Laura: **Did you see** (you see) *The Grove* yesterday?

Chloe: No, I didn't. I 1 **'ve not watched** (not watch) TV for months. What 2 **happened** (happen) since April? 3 **Has K. had** (Kate / have) her baby yet?

Laura: Yes. She 4 **had** (have) the baby weeks ago!

Chloe: What about Brett and Kylie? 5 **They started** (they / start) going out yet?

Laura: Brett and Kylie 6 **haven't been** (not be) in *The Grove* for about a month.

Chloe: Why not?

Laura: They 7 **had** (have) a terrible car accident on Kylie's birthday and Brett 8 **died** (die).

Chloe: That's awful. What 9 **did Kylie** (Kylie / do) after the accident?

Laura: It was really sad. After the accident, Kylie 10 **went** (go) back to Australia. She 11 **didn't want** (not want) to stay in England.

Chloe: 12 **Has Chris left** (Chris / leave) his wife yet?

Laura: Yes. In fact he 13 **'s already found** (already find) a new woman – Shirley. They 14 **met** (meet) on the bus!

Chloe: 15 **Has the old Mrs M. died yet** (old Mrs Moreton / die) yet?

Laura: No. She's very happy at the moment because her son, Liam, 16 **has just come** (just come) back from California. Why don't you come round and watch it with me tonight?

Chloe: I haven't got time. I'll phone tomorrow for the latest news!

Grammar highlights

Verbs *should* and *ought to*

Positive statements
She should go to bed earlier.
You ought to write to her.

Negative statements
She shouldn't go to bed so late.
You oughtn't (ought not) to speak behind her back.

Questions
Should I tell her?
Ought we to go?
What should they do?
She should go to bed earlier, shouldn't she?

- We use *should* and *ought to* when we give advice or make a strong suggestion. They mean the same, but *should* is more common, especially in questions.

Verbs *have to* and *must/mustn't*

Positive statements
I can't talk now. I have to go to work.
I couldn't talk because I had to go to work.
I'm very tired. I must go to bed.
I was very tired. I had to go to bed.

Questions
What must we do?
Do I have to tidy my room now, Mum?
We mustn't forget our tickets, must we?
We have to write a History essay, don't we?

Negative statements
You don't have to do this work if you don't want to.
At my last school, we didn't have to wear a uniform.
We mustn't make a noise. My parents are asleep.

- In positive statements, we normally use *have to* to talk about obligations which come from other people, or from routines.
- In positive statements, we normally use *must* to express the feelings and wishes of the speaker.
- *Have to* and *must* are very close in meaning. In positive statements, if you aren't sure which to use, it's safest to use *have/has to*.
- We can't use *must* to talk about past obligations. We use *had to*.

- The negatives *mustn't* and *don't /doesn't have to* have completely different meanings. We use *mustn't* to talk about prohibition. We use *don't/doesn't/didn't have to* to express a lack of obligation.
- In questions and negatives with *have to*, we normally use the auxiliaries *do, does, did*.

Would you mind? + gerund

Would you mind opening the window?
Would you mind not making a noise?

(handwritten at top) 13.5 = 65% -3

Practice

● **Verbs** *should(n't)* **and** *ought(n't) to*: **positive and negative**

1 ▷ Write pairs of sentences with *should(n't)* **and** *ought(n't) to*, **using the prompts and a phrase from the box.**

- buy new clothes all the time   • close it down
- go swimming yet   (• go to the doctor)
- learn to drive first   • tidy it   • start training
- worry about them   • use their cars so much

Darren has had a headache for two weeks.

He **should go to the doctor.**

He **ought to go to the doctor.**

1 Pollution in towns is getting worse.
People *shouldn't use their cars so much*
People *oughn't to*

2 Martha has just eaten a big meal.
She *shouldn't close it down.*
She *oughln't to — // —*

3 I want to run in the marathon next year.
You *should start training.*
You *ought to start training.*

4 Maria wants to buy a motorbike.
She *should learn to drive first.*
She *ought to learn to drive first.*

5 Jo and Tim are worried about their exams.
They *shouldn't worry about them.*
They *oughln't to worry about them*

6 My bedroom is in a terrible mess.
You *should tidy it.*
You *ought to tidy it*

7 Ben hasn't got any money.
He *shouldn't buy new clothes all the time*
He *oughln't*

8 That swimming pool is really dirty.
They *shouldn't go swimming yet.*
They *oughln't to go — // — yet.*

● **Verb** *have to*: **present simple, past simple**

2 ▷ Complete the statements and questions with the correct form of *have to.*

A: He **had to** wear a hat to the party last week.
B: Why **did he have to wear a hat?**

1 A: She *has to* get up early every day. ✓
B: What time *do you have to get up?*

2 A: I *have to* phone someone now.
B: Who *did you have to phone* ?

3 A: They *had to* go to the airport yesterday. ✗
B: Why *did you have to go to the airport*

4 A: You *had to* clean your room now.
B: Why *do you have to clean* ?

5 A: I *had to* pay a lot for my last tennis racket.
B: How much *did you to to pay* ? ✓

6 A: We *had to* wait hours for the bus yesterday.
B: How long *did you have to wait* ?

7 A: I *had to* meet Kevin now.
B: Where *did you have to met* ? ✓

8 A: Last week we *had to* take some exams.
B: How many *did you have to take* ✗

9 A: They all *had to* play silly games at the party last week. ✓
B: What sort of *did you have to play* ✓

10 A: He *has to* see the head teacher immediately. ✓
B: Why *does you have see* ?

Practice

● Verbs *have/has to* and *must/mustn't*

3 > **Read the school rules. Then complete Mrs Foster's talk with *have/has to* or *mustn't*.**

William Morris School

Please observe the following school rules at all times:

Be in class by 8.20 for morning registration.

Be in class by 1.30 for afternoon registration.

Parents, please phone the school by 9.00 if your child is ill.

Wear a helmet if you cycle to school.

Do not smoke anywhere in the school or on the way to school.

Do not eat or drink in class.

Do not wear make-up or jewellery to school.

Do not bring mobile phones to school.

Please remember that we don't have many rules here at William Morris School, but we expect you to obey the rules which we have. Firstly, you **have to** be in class for morning registration by eight twenty. You also ¹*have to* be in class at one thirty for afternoon registration.
If you're ill and can't come to school, your mother or father ²*has to* phone the school by nine o'clock. Anyone who cycles to school ³*has to* wear a helmet. Smoking is, of course, forbidden. You ⁴*mustn't* smoke anywhere in the school grounds or on the way to school. You ⁵*mustn't* eat or drink in class and you ⁶*mustn't* wear make-up or jewellery to school. Lastly, you ⁷*mustn't* bring mobile phones to school. Is that clear?

● Verbs *mustn't* and *don't/doesn't have to*

4 > **Complete the sentences with *mustn't* or *don't/doesn't have to*.**

You **mustn't** swim in the river. It's very dangerous.

We **don't have to** stand up when teachers come into the room, but we usually do.

1 We *don't have to* do sport after school but we can if we want to.

2 You *mustn't* make a noise. There's an exam in room fifteen.

3 It's Saturday tomorrow so he *doesn't have to* get up early. He can sleep until ten.

4 You *mustn't* go into the laboratory without a teacher. Please wait outside.

5 Mark's lucky. He *doesn't have to* wear a uniform at his school.

6 You *mustn't* tell anybody. It's a secret.

7 Don't worry. There's plenty of time. We *don't have to* run.

8 She can bring James if she likes, but she *doesn't have* bring him.

9 Registration is at eight twenty. You *mustn't* be late.

Practice

● **Verbs** *should, must* **and** *have to* **with question tags**

5 Complete the questions with the correct tags.

We should take the number 33 bus, **shouldn't we?**

1 He doesn't have to do the washing-up,

.... *Does he* ....?

2 Martha should choose the music,

.... *Shouldn't she* ....?

3 We didn't have to do any homework,

.... *Did we* ....?

4 They must decide by tomorrow,

.... *Must they* ....?

5 Rachel has to answer, ...*doesn't she*...?

6 They mustn't be late, ...*must they*...?

7 We have to help Mum, ...*do we*...?

8 Sandra shouldn't be here, ...*should she*...?

9 He had to leave, ...*didn't he*...?

10 You don't have to pay, ...*do you*...?

11 The dog had to stay outside, ...*didn't it*...?

12 They didn't have to bring anything,

.... *did they* ....?

● *Would you mind?* **+ gerund**

6 Match the commands with the reasons. Then write polite requests with *Would you mind?*

Look after our goldfish. **i**
1 Buy some aspirins. ☐ *h*
2 Turn the music down. ☐ *d*
3 Lend me your bike. ☐ *b*
4 Open the window. ☐ *g*
5 Open the door. ☐ *a*
6 Make the dinner. ☐ *c*
7 Help me with this suitcase. ☐ *e*
8 Sign the visitors' book. ☐ *f*

a) The cat wants to go out.
b) I'm late for school.
c) I'm too tired.
d) I'm trying to sleep.
e) It's terribly heavy.
f) It's one of the club rules.
g) It's very hot in here.
h) Mum's got a headache.
i) We're going on holiday.

Would you mind looking after our goldfish?
We're going on holiday.

1 Would you mind buying some aspirins? Mum's got a headache.

2 Would you mind turning the music down? I'm trying to sleep.

3 Would you mind lending me your bike? I'm late for school.

4 Would you mind opening the window? It's very hot here.

5 Would you mind opening the door? The cat want to go out.

6 Would you mind making the dinner? I'm too tired.

7 Would you mind helping me with this suitcase. It's terribly heavy.

8 Would you mind signing the visitors book. It's one of the club rules.

Grammar highlights

Present perfect continuous with *for* and *since*

Positive statements

Short form	Long form
I've been talking.	I have been talking.
You've been talking.	You have been talking.
He's been talking.	He has been talking.
She's been talking.	She has been talking.
We've been talking.	We have been talking.
They've been talking.	They have been talking.

Negative statements

Short form	Long form
I haven't been working.	I have not been working.
You haven't been working.	You have not been working.
He hasn't been working.	He has not been working.
She hasn't been working.	She has not been working.
We haven't been working.	We have not been working.
They haven't been working.	They have not been working.

Questions

Have I been waiting?
Have you been waiting?
Has he been waiting?
Has she been waiting?
Have we been waiting?
Have they been waiting?

Short answers

Positive	Negative
Yes, I/you have.	No, I/you haven't.
Yes, he/she has.	No, he/she hasn't.
Yes, we/they have.	No, we/they haven't.

Offers: *Would you like me to? / Shall I?*

Would you like me to carry that?
Shall I open the window?

● One use of the present perfect continuous is to talk about events and actions which began in the past and are still happening at the present moment.

● The present perfect continuous can be used to answer the question *How long?*, e.g. *How long have you been waiting? I've been waiting since eight o'clock/ for three hours. I haven't been waiting very long.*

Practice

● **Present perfect continuous with** *for* **and** *since:* **positive statements**

1 > Use the prompts to write sentences in the present perfect continuous with *for* **or** *since.*

Felix is watching the goldfish.
He started watching them an hour ago.

> ***He has been watching them for an hour.***

Maria is studying Chinese.
She started studying it in 1997.

> ***She has been studying it since 1997.***

1 Sandra feels ill.
She started to feel ill a week ago.

....

2 They're playing tennis.
They started playing at two o'clock.
They have been playing at 2 o'clock

3 We're travelling around South America.
We started travelling in June.
We have been travelling in June

4 I'm doing the washing-up.
I started doing it an hour ago.
I've been doing it an ha.

5 It's snowing.
It started snowing at two o'clock.
It has been snowing at 2 o'cl

6 Andy is reading *War and Peace.*
He started it months ago.

....
....

● **Present perfect continuous with** *for* **and** *since:* **questions and answers**

2 > Write questions with *How long?* **and the present perfect continuous, and answers with** *for* **or** *since,* **using the prompts.**

Q: Maria / speak / on the phone
A: fifteen minutes

Q: ***How long has Maria been speaking on the phone?***

A: ***For fifteen minutes.***

1 Q: your father / read / the newspaper
A: an hour and a half
Q: *How long has m.f. been reading the N.*
A: *For an hour and a half*

2 Q: the cat / watch / the bird
A: four o'clock
Q: *How long has the cat been watching*
A: *Since*

3 Q: it / rain
A: two thirty
Q: *How long has it been raining*
A: *Since*

4 Q: she / grate / the cheese
A: about ten minutes
Q: *How long has she been grating th.*
A: *For*

5 Q: they / lie / in the sun
A: breakfast
Q: *How long have they lying in th*
A: *Since breakfast*

6 Q: you / live / in Ohio
A: March
Q: ....
A: *Since march*

7 Q: we / wait / for the bus
A: forty minutes
Q: ....
A: *For 40 min*

8 Q: the pizza / cook / in the oven
A: one o'clock
Q: ....
A: *Since one o'clock*

Practice

● Present perfect continuous with *for* and *since*

3 ⟩ **Match the activities with the time phrases. Then write sentences in the present perfect continuous.**

People (watch) TV programmes   **c**

1 Humans (live) on Earth   *for*   **H**
2 People (travel) in space   *for since*   **E**
3 People (drive) cars   *for since*   **A**
4 Madonna (make) records   *since*   **G**
5 Leonardo DiCaprio (work) as an actor   *Sept*   **I**
6 People (write)   *for*   **B**
7 People (ride) bicycles   *since*   **D**   A
8 I (do) this exercise   *for*   **E**

```
a) 1790.
b) about 5,000 years.
c) about 60 years.
d) about 1900.
e) about five minutes.
f) 1961.
g) 1982.
h) about 100,000 years.
i) he was five.
```

People have been watching TV programmes for about 60 years.

1 ....
2 ....
3 ....
4 ....
5 ....
6 ....
7 ....
8 ....

● Present perfect continuous and past simple

4 ⟩ **Complete the conversation by putting the verbs in brackets in the past simple or present perfect continuous.**

Miranda: Sorry I'm late. How long ***have you been waiting*** (you / wait)?

Nick: Don't worry. I [1]..................... (not wait) very long. I [2].............. (get) here about ten minutes ago. By the way, why is your hair wet? [3].......................... (it / rain)?

Miranda: Yes, it has. And I [4]................ (come) by bike so I got wet, of course.

Nick: How long [5]............................ (you / use) a bike to get around London?

Miranda: I [6].............. (buy) this bike two weeks ago and I [7]........................ (ride) it every day since I got it. Are you OK, Nick? You look tired.

Nick: I [8]................ (not sleep) well last night and I [9].................... (feel) tired all day.

Miranda: Perhaps you need to do more sport.

Nick: I [10]...................... (have) a riding lesson in Richmond Park yesterday evening.

Miranda: Was that fun?

Nick: Yes, I [11]................ (enjoy) it.

Miranda: How long [12].............................. (you / learn) to ride?

Nick: About three months. You should come with me some time.

Miranda: I think I prefer riding my bike. It doesn't kick or bite!

113

Practice

● **Offers:** *Would you like me to?* **and** *Shall I?*

5〉 **Complete the offers in the letter with** *Would you like me* **or** *Shall I?* **Then match Maria's offers with Rebecca's answers.**

Dear Rebecca,

I'm writing because I heard from Michael about your broken leg.

I hope you're feeling better now. Are you getting bored? a) <u>Would you like me</u> to bring you some books or magazines?

Is the food in hospital OK? If not,

b) _____ bring you some fruit? c) _____ to bring anything else? Shampoo? Writing paper? Stamps?

And another thing. Who is looking after your dog? d) _____ to take him for walks sometimes? What about your library books? e) _____ take them back to the library for you?

f) _____ bring you the new History notes?

g) _____ to lend you my mobile phone? Call me soon.

Lots of love,

Maria

1 ☐ ....
....
Oh, yes. Can you please get me some envelopes?

2 ☐ **a** *Would you like me to bring you some books or magazines?*
Yes, please. I'd like *Big Surf* magazine.

3 ☐ ....
I'd love some grapes.

4 ☐ ....
....
That would be great. I'll pay for my calls.

5 ☐ ....
....
It's OK. Mum's looking after him.

6 ☐ ....
....
It's OK. Jim's already taken them back.

7 ☐ ....
....
You are joking, aren't you?

Unit 11

Grammar highlights

Verbs *will/won't*, *may* or *might* for predictions

Positive statements

We will be there at six. (It's definite.)
We'll bring Eva. (It's definite.)
Jackie may/might come too. (It's possible.)

Negative statements

We won't be late. (It's definite.)
We may/might not come by car. (It's possible.)

Questions	Short answers
Will we know anybody?	Yes, you will.
Will Andy be there?	He may/might.
Will there be a party after the match?	No, there won't.

First conditional: *if/unless* clause + *'ll (will)/won't*

If I see one, I'll buy one for you.
I'll buy one for you if I see one.
If you don't leave now, you'll miss the train.
Unless you leave now, you'll miss the train.
You'll miss the train unless you leave now.
If you don't water the plants, they won't grow.

- We use *will/won't* to talk about definite future events.
- We use *may/might* to talk about possible future events.
  There is no difference between *may* and *might* in this case.

- There is no short form of *may* or *might*.
- *Mightn't* is the short form of the negative *might not*.
  There is no short form of the negative *may not*.

- The first conditional is used to describe a possible future event and its consequences.
- *If* or *unless* can introduce a first conditional clause. *Unless* means *if ... not*, e.g. *I won't phone if there isn't a problem. = I won't phone unless there's a problem.*
- In first conditional sentences, the verb in the *if/unless* clause is in the present simple tense. The verb in the main clause is often in the future simple tense *(will/won't)*.
- *Will* and *won't* can be replaced in the main clause by *may (not)*, *might (not)* or *can*.
- When the *if/unless* clause comes first, we separate it from the main clause with a comma, e.g. *If I find the photo, I'll send it to you.*
- When the main clause comes first, there is no comma between it and the *if/unless* clause, e.g. *They may not come if the weather is bad. They won't cycle unless the weather is good.*

Practice

● Verbs *will/won't* **for predictions**

1 ⟩ **Match the sentence halves. Then write the complete sentences.**

What will life be like f

1 People will go to ✗ h
2 The Earth will be a ✓ d
3 The President of the USA will be ✗ a
4 Most people will be ✓ i
5 People will eat special chemicals ✓ c
6 We will get all our electricity ✓ b
7 Nobody will go ✓ j
8 Students will have all their lessons ✓ e
9 Lots of people will have ✗ g

a) a woman.
b) from the sun, the wind and the sea.
c) instead of food.
d) much hotter place than now.
e) on the Internet.
f) one hundred years from now?
g) robots to do the housework.
h) the moon for their holidays.
i) to school.
j) vegetarians.

What will life be like one hundred years from now?

1 ....
....
2 ....
....
3 ....
....
4 ....
5 ....
....
6 ....
....
7 ....
8 ....
....
9 ....
....

● Verbs *will/won't, might* **for predictions**

2 ⟩ **Complete the conversations with *will, 'll, won't* or *might*. If both *'ll* and *will* are possible, use *'ll*.**

1 A: When **will** my photos be ready?
   B: They probably ¹ *won't* take very long. Two hours at the most, so they ² *will* definitely be ready by four o'clock.
   A: How much ³ *will* they cost?
   B: Ten pounds, probably. But they ⁴ *will* be a little more. It depends.
   A: I see. I ⁵ *will* try to be back at two to pick them up. But I ⁶ *might* be a bit late.

2 A: I'm worried about my driving test. I probably ⁷ *won't* be able to start the car!
   B: Don't be silly. Of course, you ⁸ *will* .
   A: ⁹ *Will* you be angry if I don't pass?
   B: Yes, I ¹⁰ *will* ! I need you to drive me to the airport tomorrow!

3 A: I'm afraid you ¹¹ .... be able to go out this evening. I want you to stay at home and look after Claire.
   B: Nick ¹² *might* be annoyed with me.
   A: No, he ¹³ *won't* . You can invite him here for the evening.
   B: I'm sure he ¹⁴ *won't* come. He hates small children.
   A: I'm not so sure. He likes you, so he ¹⁵ *might* come. Why don't you call him and ask?

4 A: Is Cathy going to play in the match on Saturday?
   B: She ¹⁶ *might* but I don't know for sure. She's got a bad cold at the moment and she ¹⁷ *might* still be ill on Saturday.

Practice

● First conditional with *if*

3 Match the sentence halves. Check your answers. Then write sentences in the first conditional.

The Snapshot Superstitions Quiz

a black cat (walk) in front of you	**g**	a) he or she (have) bad luck.
1 you (be) lucky at cards		b) there (be) good weather the next day.
2 you (eat) an apple every day		c) you (be) unlucky in love.
3 you (break) a mirror		d) you (not be) friends for very long.
4 a friend (give) you a knife as a present		e) you (have) bad dreams.
5 you (eat) cheese at night		f) you (have) bad luck for seven years.
6 somebody (walk) under a ladder		g) you (have) good luck.
7 the sky (be) red at night		h) you (never need) to go to the doctor.

If a black cat walks in front of you, you'll have good luck.

1 ....

2 ....

3 ....

4 ....

5 ....

6 ....

7 ....

117

Practice

● First conditional with *if/unless* clause

4 > Write the advertisements, using the prompts with *if* or *unless* and the verbs in brackets.

L.A.
POLICE RABBIT
If you like comedies, you'll love this film.

you (like) comedies / you (love) this film

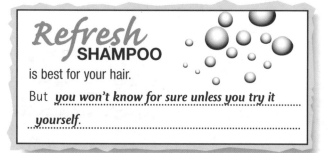

Refresh **SHAMPOO**
is best for your hair.
But *you won't know for sure unless you try it yourself*.

you (not know) for sure / you (try) it yourself

1

THE SPORTS STORE

we (not have) your shoe size / we (give) you a free tennis racket

2

Snips HAIRDRESSERS

You (not pay) a penny / you (be) happy with your new hairstyle

3

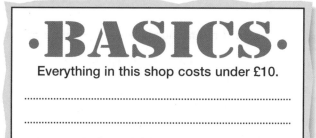

·BASICS·
Everything in this shop costs under £10.

you (want) expensive clothes / we (not be) right for you

4

SAFARI *Sixteen*

You (not like) our holiday camps / you (enjoy) adventures

5

ZEST SPORTS CLUB
Tell your friends about us.

a friend of yours (join) the club / we (give) you a free sports bag

6

Problem skin?
Hide your spots with SPOTLESS Cream!

Spotless

Your best friends (not know) about your spots / you (tell) them

Grammar highlights

The passive: present simple

Some jokes are told in every country.
These gates aren't locked at night.
Where is the sugar kept?
Paper is made from wood, isn't it?
Yes, it is.
Aren't you expected to do any homework?
No, I'm not.
The man in the photo is wanted by the police.

● The present simple passive is formed with the present tense of the verb *to be* and the past participle of the main verb.

The passive: past simple

We were invited to a jazz concert.
She wasn't told about the broken window.
When were the Pyramids built?
This watch was given to me by my great grandfather.
The telephone was invented by Bell, wasn't it?
Yes, it was.
Weren't the papers delivered this morning?
No, they weren't.

● The past simple passive is formed with the past tense of the verb *to be* and the past participle of the main verb.

● We use the passive when we are more interested in the action or process than the person or thing that causes it, e.g. *A lot of money was stolen from the bank.* (= We don't know who stole it.) *Are the animals treated well?* (= It's not important who treats them well.)

● If we want to say who does the action or what causes it, we use *by*, e.g. *This picture was painted by a girl in my class.*

● We do not need to repeat the verb *to be* if we are giving a list of actions in the passive, e.g. *The apples are washed, dried and delivered to the storeroom.*

Practice

● **Present and past simple passive: positive statements**

1 > **Complete the sentences with a verb from the box in the present or past simple passive.**

| • allow • break • serve • deliver • give |
| • grow • keep • invent • leave • make |
| • open • show |

The world high jump record **_was broken_** last week.

1 Two different films _are shown_ in this cinema every day.

2 We _are_ to use calculators in our last Maths exam.

3 Macy's, the largest department store in the world, _Was open_ in New York in 1858.

4 In Britain, milk .... to people's houses. It .... at the front door.

5 The trees in this forest .... just to produce paper.

6 The first paper .... from papyrus plants in ancient Egypt.

7 Paper money .... in China in the seventh century.

8 Breakfast .... from seven to nine in the dining room. Please do not be late.

9 We .... lots of homework yesterday.

10 Zoos are places where animals .... in cages.

● **Present and past simple passive: questions and negative statements**

2 > **Rewrite these sentences in the passive.**

Where did they grow these enormous tomatoes?
Where were these enormous tomatoes grown?

1 They don't use pesticides on organic farms.

....

....

2 When did they build the Great Wall of China?
When were the Great Wall of China built?

3 They didn't leave the keys in the car.

....

....

4 They don't play cricket in America.

....

....

5 Where did they find the gold watch?
Where were the gold watch found?

6 Why don't people grow tea in Europe?
Why aren't tea in Europe grown?

7 Why don't you allow us to watch TV?
Why aren't us to watch TV allowed?

8 How much do they pay you a week?
How much are you a week payd?

9 Why didn't somebody stop them?
Why weren't them stoped?

10 Why didn't you tell me about the problem?
Why weren't me about the problem told?

Practice

● **Present and past simple passive: questions and answers**

3 ⟩ Match the words in Box A to the words in Box B. Check your answers. Then write questions and answers in the present or past simple passive.

The Snapshot General Knowledge Quiz

Box A		Box B
How often / American presidential elections / hold?	**h**	a) 1876
1 When / the Pyramids / build?	☐	b) 1918
2 Where / women / first give / the vote?	☐	c) 1985
3 When / telephone / invent?	☐	d) 44BC
4 What / plastic / make from?	☐	e) metal
5 Which game / play / at Wimbledon?	☐	f) football
6 When / British women / first allow / to vote?	☐	g) New Zealand
7 Which game / play / at Wembley Stadium?	☐	(h) every four years)
8 When / Julius Caesar / kill?	☐	i) more than 4,000 years ago
9 When / the *Titanic* / find?	☐	j) oil
10 What / electric guitar strings / made of?	☐	k) tennis

Q: *How often are American presidential elections held?*

A: *They are held every four years.*

1 Q: ....
A: ....
....

2 Q: ....
....
A: ....
....

3 Q: ....
A: ....

4 Q: ....
A: ....

5 Q: ....
A: ....

6 Q: ....
....
A: ....
....

7 Q: ....
....
A: ....
....

8 Q: ....
A: ....

9 Q: ....
A: ....

10 Q: ....
A: ....
....

ANSWERS: 1i); 2g); 3o); 4j); 5k); 6b); 7f); 8d); 9c); 10e)

Practice

● Present and past simple passive

4 ⟩ Complete the text, putting the verbs in brackets in the present or past simple, active or passive.

Tea
– the most popular drink in the world

India, Sri Lanka and China ...*grow*........... (grow) most of the world's tea. The tea plant can grow to 12 metres high, but it *is usually cut* (usually cut) to 1.5 metres. The leaves [1] .... (not pick) until the plant is about five years old.

Tea [2] .... (produce) like this. First the tea leaves [3] .... (pick). Then they [4] .... (take) to special rooms to dry. They [5] .... (leave) in these rooms for a day. Then the leaves [6] .... (break) by machines. This [7] .... (allow) the oil to come out of the leaves. Next the leaves [8] .... (put) into ovens. When the tea leaves [9] .... (come) out of the ovens, they [10] .... (pack) in wooden boxes. Some of the tea [11] .... (export) and some of it [12] .... (keep) in the country where it was grown.

Tea [13] .... (probably discover) in China about 5,000 years ago. According to one story, Emperor Shang Yeng was drinking hot water in his garden when some leaves [14] .... (fall) off a wild tea bush into his cup. He [15] .... (love) the drink and soon tea bushes [16] .... (plant) all over China. For a long time, tea [17] .... (use) as money in China. In the fourteenth century, a good horse [18] .... (cost) about 68 kilos of tea.

Tea [19] .... (not bring) to England until 1657. At first only rich people [20] .... (drink) it because it was expensive. But it soon [21] .... (become) a very popular drink. Most people now [22] .... (make) tea with tea bags. In fact, every day in Britain, 150 million cups of tea [23] .... (make) from tea bags.

Unit 13

Grammar highlights

Pronouns: *someone, anyone, no one, everyone*

There's someone at the front door.
Has anyone seen my keys?
No one sent me a birthday card this year.
Has everyone got a ticket?

Pronouns: *something, anything, nothing, everything*

I've got something funny to tell you.
She didn't have anything interesting to say.
There's nothing for us to do in this town.
He gave everything to charity.

Pronouns: *somewhere, anywhere, nowhere, everywhere*

Let's go somewhere different this evening.
'Where shall we go?' 'Anywhere. You choose.'
The club was very crowded. There was nowhere to sit.
I've looked everywhere for my purse but I can't find it.

Second conditional: *if* **clause +** *'d(would)/ wouldn't*

If I knew her address, I'd send her a birthday card.
It would take her an hour to get to school if she didn't have a bike.
If you could meet one famous person, who would you choose?
I wouldn't tell them about the party if I were you.

- We can also use *-body* instead of *-one*: *somebody, anybody, nobody, everybody,* e.g. *I didn't know anybody at the party.*

- Generally we use *someone, somebody, something* and *somewhere* in positive statements. We also use them in questions when we offer things, e.g. *Would you like something to drink?*

- Generally we use *anyone, anybody, anything* and *anywhere* in questions and negative statements.

- We use *anyone, anybody, anything* and *anywhere* when we mean 'it doesn't matter who, what, where,' e.g. *'Who shall I bring to your party?' 'Anyone.' 'What would you like to drink?' 'Anything.'*

- When we use the negative words *no one, nothing* and *nowhere*, we do not use a negative verb, e.g. *He did nothing.* (= He didn't do anything.) *I saw no one.* (= I didn't see anyone.)

- All these pronouns take singular verbs, e.g. *No one knows the answer. Everyone has to bring a notebook and pencil.* But we often use *their* and *they* after these pronouns, e.g. *Somebody has left their keys here.* (*their keys* = his or her keys)

- We use the second conditional to talk about unreal or unlikely situations, or to give advice.

- *If I were you* is more common than *If I was you.*

Practice

● **Pronouns:** *some-, any-, no-, every- +*
thing, one, where

1 〉 **Complete the sentences with the correct pronoun.**

Turn the tap off. There's water __everywhere__.

1   I didn't want .... to eat because
I felt sick.

2   The house was a mess after the party. There were
bottles and glasses ....

3   They slept on the beach because they had
.... to stay.

4   He's upset about .... but he won't
tell .... his problem.

5   'Where shall we eat?' ' ....
I don't mind.'

6   There's .... at the door. Can you
go and open it?

7   We're bored. There's .... to do.

8   Listen carefully, ... I'm not going
to say this twice.

9   I don't want to buy anything in this shop.
.... is too expensive.

10 Let's find .... quiet to sit.

● **Second conditional**

2 〉 **Use the prompts to write sentences in the
second conditional.**

If I (be) you / I (not play) with those matches.

If I were you, I wouldn't play with those matches.

1   If you (know) him better / you (not lend) him your
tent.
*If you knew him better, you'd
not lend him your tent.*

2   What (you / do) / if you (find) £20 on the ground?
....
....

3   (you / spend) the money or (you / save) it / if you
(win) £1,000?
....
....

4   Where (you / go) / if you (can) travel anywhere in
the world?
....
....

5   I (not go) out with him / if I (be) her.
I wouldn't ... if I was
....

6   If I (not be) late for work / I (help) you.
*If I wasnt , I would help
you*

7   If you (can) be anyone, anywhere, at any time in
history / who (you / choose) to be?
*If you could be ... who
would you choose to be*

8   I (not have) to help with the washing-up / if you
(buy) a dishwasher
....
....

9   What (you / say) to Jim Carrey / if you (meet) him?
....
....

Practice

● **Second conditional**

3 ⟩ **Complete the quiz questions using the verbs in brackets. Then circle your reaction.**

  a man with a knife (ask) for your money
1 you (find) a snake in your tent when camping
2 you (cut) your finger very badly while cooking
3 you (see) smoke coming out of a neighbour's house

4 a shark (come) near you in the sea
5 your boyfriend /girlfriend (go) out with someone else
6 you (not have) enough money to pay your bill in a restaurant
7 you (hear) strange noises in the kitchen at night

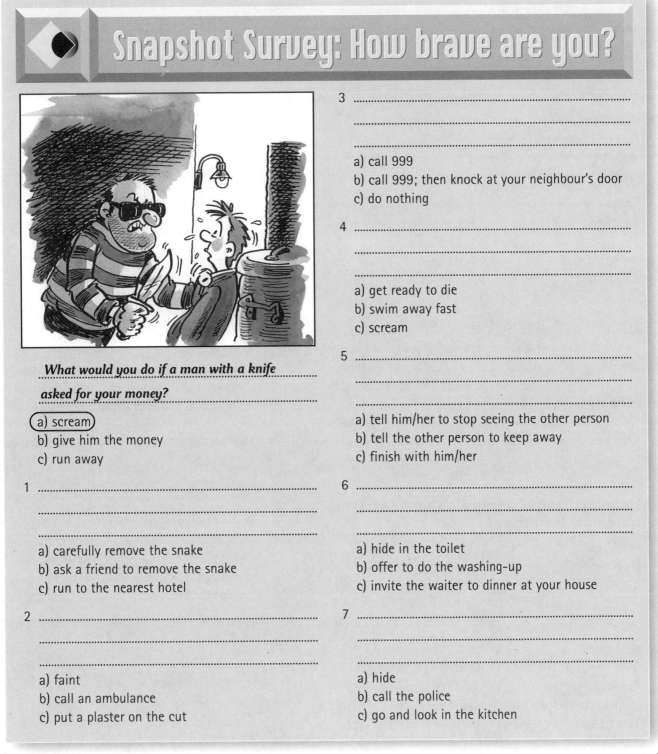

Snapshot Survey: How brave are you?

What would you do if a man with a knife asked for your money?

  ⓐ scream
  b) give him the money
  c) run away

1 ....
  ....
  ....
  a) carefully remove the snake
  b) ask a friend to remove the snake
  c) run to the nearest hotel

2 ....
  ....
  ....
  a) faint
  b) call an ambulance
  c) put a plaster on the cut

3 ....
  ....
  ....
  a) call 999
  b) call 999; then knock at your neighbour's door
  c) do nothing

4 ....
  ....
  ....
  a) get ready to die
  b) swim away fast
  c) scream

5 ....
  ....
  ....
  a) tell him/her to stop seeing the other person
  b) tell the other person to keep away
  c) finish with him/her

6 ....
  ....
  ....
  a) hide in the toilet
  b) offer to do the washing-up
  c) invite the waiter to dinner at your house

7 ....
  ....
  ....
  a) hide
  b) call the police
  c) go and look in the kitchen

Grammar highlights

Remember

Past perfect simple

Positive statements
She had finished the job.
They'd already gone.

Negative statements
She hadn't made any mistakes.
They hadn't waited.

Questions
Had he opened his letters?
Hadn't they met before?
You'd already told him, hadn't you?

Short answers

Positive	Negative
Yes, he had.	No, he hadn't.
Yes, they had.	No, they hadn't.
Yes, I had.	No, I hadn't.

- We form the past perfect simple with the auxiliary *had* + the past participle.
- We use the past perfect simple tense to describe an event in the past that happened before another event in the past, e.g. *When I got there, he had left.* (= He left first; then I got there.) *She didn't want to come to the cinema because she had already seen the film.*

too many, too much, not enough

He couldn't understand the newspaper article because there were too many difficult words in it.
I left the concert because there was too much classical music and not enough jazz.
The film was boring because there weren't enough jokes.
She didn't enjoy the book because there wasn't enough humour.

- We use *too many* with plural countable nouns and *too much* with uncountable nouns. We use *(not) enough* with plural countable and uncountable nouns.

Reported requests and commands (verb + object + infinitive)

Positive

Direct speech	Reported speech
'Please help me.'	She wanted me to help her.
'Please give me a lift.'	She asked me to give her a lift.
'Drive carefully.'	She told me to drive carefully.

Negative

Direct speech	Reported speech
'Don't leave.'	He didn't want me to leave.
'Please don't tell anyone.'	He asked me not to tell anyone.
'Don't go too fast.'	He told me not to go too fast.

- We often use the imperative in direct requests and commands. We use the verbs *tell*, *ask* and *want* plus an object plus the infinitive with *to* when we want to report requests or commands.

Practice

● Past perfect simple

1 > **Read about the situations and write sentences in the past perfect simple.**

My plate was empty and the cat was smiling.
(It / eat / my dinner)

It had eaten my dinner.

1 You went to see Joe but he wasn't at home.
(He / go / out)

....

2 I was pleased to see Ann after all this time.
(I / not see / her / for five years)

....

....

3 We arrived at the cinema late last night.
(Luckily, the film / not yet start)

....

....

4 Sue couldn't come to our party.
(She / already / agree / to go to Andy's party)

....

....

5 You saw a friend from primary school.
(She / not change / a lot)

....

6 Sonia didn't want to go swimming.
(She / just wash / her hair)

....

● Past perfect simple

2 > **Complete each sentence with the correct ending. Put the verbs in the past perfect simple.**

b I ran home *because I had forgotten to turn the grill off*.

1 ☐ We lost the game ....

....

2 ☐ She wasn't wearing glasses ....

....

3 ☐ He was upset yesterday ....

....

4 ☐ I threw the newspaper away ....

....

5 ☐ We gave her some money ....

....

6 ☐ His mother shouted at him ....

....

7 ☐ The ground was very dry ....

....

8 ☐ The house was very quiet ....

....

a) because he (have) a fight with his girlfriend.
b) because I (forget) to turn the grill off.
c) because he (not tidy) his room.
d) because I (already read) it.
e) because it (not rain) for months.
f) because everyone (go) to bed.
g) because she (leave) them at home.
h) because she (spend) all hers.
i) because we (not train) hard enough.

Practice

● Past perfect or past simple

3 ➤ Use the prompts to complete the sentences in two different ways. Use the past perfect and past simple in each pair of sentences.

I left the party early because
a) I (not know) anyone there ·

I didn't know anyone there.
....

b) I (agree) to meet Sophie at ten

I had agreed to meet Sophie at ten.
....

1 When I got to Sophie's place,
a) she (already leave)

....

b) I (cannot) find her

....

2 I began walking back to the party. I stopped when
a) I (walk) about 300 metres

....

b) I (see) a tall girl with a guitar

....

3 It was Natasha Ward.
a) I (not see) her for three years

....

b) She (be) really pleased to see me

....

4 I invited her to come to the party with me but
a) she (not like) the idea very much

....

b) she (already agree) to eat out with a friend

....

5 She invited me to come too and I agreed because
a) I (want) to get to know her better

....

b) I (not have) anything to eat all day

....

6 At the restaurant we met Natasha's friend. It was Sophie,
a) who (forget) about our plans for the evening

....

b) who (be) very surprised to see me with Natasha

....

● too many, too much, not enough

4 ➤ Complete the sentences with *too many, too much* **or** *n't enough.*

I couldn't write my name in the gap.
There was __**n't enough**__ space.

1 We can't make lemonade because there are ....
.... lemons.

2 The disco was very crowded. There were ....
.... people and there was ....
space to dance.

3 She ate .... chocolates and now she feels sick.

4 There were .... glasses so we drank out of cups.

5 There's .... sugar in this coffee. It's really sweet.

6 They couldn't finish the test. There were ....
.... questions.

7 Please don't make .... noise. My little sister is asleep.

5 ➤ Complete the doctor's comments with the present continuous of the verbs in brackets and *too many, too much* **or** *n't ... enough.*

- (take) exercise

You aren't taking enough exercise.
....

+ (eat) cakes and sweets

You're eating too many cakes and sweets.
....

1 – (get) fresh air

....

2 + (drink) coffee

....

3 + (have) late nights

....

4 – (do) exercise

....

5 – (eat) fruit and vegetables

....

6 + (do) work

....

Practice

● Reported requests and commands

6 > Read the film director's notes. What did he tell each person to do?

First Take
FILM PRODUCTIONS

hairdresser – change Antonio's hairstyle

security guards – don't open the gates until 6 a.m.

1 Leonardo – arrive an hour earlier on Wednesday

2 make-up artist – give Kate darker lipstick

3 electricians – put up coloured lights for the nightclub scene

4 dancers – don't look at the camera

5 extras – be at the reception desk by 8 a.m.

6 Sam – don't phone me before 7 p.m.

He told the hairdresser to change Antonio's hairstyle.

He told the security guards not to open the gates until 6 a.m.

1 ....

....

2 ....

....

3 ....

....

4 ....

....

5 ....

....

6 ....

....

● Reported requests and commands

7 > Match the requests in boxes a) to i) with the sentence beginnings. Then complete each sentence with the correct reported request.

[h] Lucy was making a terrible noise so I told **her to be quiet**.

....

1 ☐ I wanted to have a shower so I told

....

2 ☐ Mick was driving very fast so I told

....

3 ☐ Maria was upset about her exam so I told

....

4 ☐ I couldn't hear the teacher so I asked

....

5 ☐ The goldfish were very hungry so I asked

....

6 ☐ They had dirty hands so I didn't want

....

7 ☐ I was really hungry so I didn't want

....

8 ☐ Pete and I were going to a sixties party and we wanted ....

a) Can you feed them, Andy?

b) Can you take a photo of us, Irma?

c) Could you repeat the question please, Sir?

d) Don't be too long in the bathroom, Dave.

e) Don't eat all the spaghetti, Simon.

f) Don't touch my drawings.

g) Don't worry!

(h)) Please be quiet!

i) Slow down!

Grammar highlights

Remember

Verb *used to*

Positive statements

I used to have short hair (but I've grown it).
There used to be a school here (but there isn't now).
She used to work in a shop (but she doesn't now).

Negative statements

I didn't use to have long hair (but I do now).
There didn't use to be a cinema here (but there is now).
She didn't use to work in a restaurant (but she does now).

Questions

Did you use to like having short hair?
Didn't there use to be a cinema here?
Where did she use to work?

Short answers

Positive	Negative
Yes, I did.	No, I didn't.
Yes, there did.	No, there didn't.

● We use *used to* to talk about things which were true in the past but are not true now.

so and *such a/an* + adjective + noun for exclamations

She's so good at art!
She's such a good painter!
It was such an amazing holiday!
There were such exciting activities!

● We use *so* with an adjective and *such (a/an)* with an adjective followed by a noun.

so and *such* with a clause of result

He was so surprised (that) he couldn't speak.
They were so happy (that) they danced in the street.
It was such a boring book (that) I couldn't read it.
They were such stupid jokes (that) nobody laughed at them.

● When we use *so* or *such* in result clauses, we can omit *that*, e.g. *The book was so boring that I couldn't read it. It was such a boring book that I couldn't read it.* Or: *The book was so boring I couldn't read it. It was such a boring book I couldn't read it.*

Practice

● *Used to*: **positive and negative statements**

1 ⟩ **Write the sentences with** *used to/didn't use to*
and the present or past simple.

He (play) a lot of football but now he just (watch)
it on TV.
He used to play a lot of football but now he just
watches it on TV.

1 She (not like) tea but she (drink) a lot of it these
   days.

   ....

   ....

2 There (be) a lot of cars in this town but now
   everybody (ride) bicycles.

   ....

   ....

3 He (not take) any exercise but now he (go) for a
   run every day.

   ....

   ....

4 My grandparents (not travel) outside Britain but
   last year they (go) to Spain for the first time.

   ....

   ....

5 We (have) a dog but it (die) a year ago.

   ....

   ....

6 You (talk) all the time but you (be) very quiet these
   days.

   ....

   ....

7 People (read) a lot in their free time but now they
   (watch) TV.

   ....

   ....

8 Sandra (live) in Bristol but she (move) to Penzance
   last month.

   ....

   ....

● *Used to*: **positive and negative statements**

2 ⟩ **Use the prompts to write sentences with** *used*
to/didn't use to ... but now he doesn't/does.

Seth got married last year and changed a lot.
He stopped:
seeing lots of different girls.
1 going to clubs every night.
2 riding a motorbike.
3 spending all his money.
4 watching football on TV.

   Seth used to see lots of different girls but now
   he doesn't.

1 ....

   ....

2 ....

   ....

3 ....

   ....

4 ....

He started:
to like children.
5 to save money .
6 to work hard at his job.
7 to go to a sports club.
8 to go to bed early.

   He didn't use to like children but now he does.

5 ....

   ....

6 ....

   ....

7 ....

   ....

8 ....

● *Used to*: **positive and negative statements**

Practice

● *Used to:* **question forms**

3 > Read the text. Then write the interviewer's questions, using a verb from the box in the present simple or with *use to.*

> • live   (• earn)   • get up   • have   • travel

She used to be a **st★r**

···

Three years ago, Emma Forbes was the star of the TV show *Twenty Something*. But when the show ended, Emma couldn't get another acting job. We interviewed her at Sandways Supermarket in west London, where she now works as a cashier.

How much did you use to earn?
About £150,000 a year.

How much do you earn now?
About £13,000 a year.

❶ .... ?
In a big house in Hampstead.

❷ .... now?
In a small flat in Acton.

❸ .... ?
About ten or eleven in the morning.

❹ .... now?
At seven. I have to be at the supermarket by eight in the morning.

❺ .... a lot?
Yes, I did. I used to go all over the world for my work and I also used to take a lot of holidays.

❻ .... a lot now?
No, I don't. I usually go to Cornwall for two weeks in the summer.

❼ .... a lot of parties?
Yes. People used to come to my home two or three times a week. It was great fun.

❽ .... a lot of parties now?
No, but I invite my best friends round for my birthday.

● *Used to:* **all forms**

4 > Complete the conversation between Tara and her great-grandmother, Rose, with the correct form of *used to.*

Rose: I'm ninety-eight years old and I can tell you things have changed a lot in my lifetime. Families **used to** be much bigger and children [1].................. be much more polite.

Tara: [2].................. women .... do all the boring jobs?

Rose: Well, my mother [3].................. stay at home and do all the housework. And all the girls, my four sisters and I, [4].................. help her. The boys did nothing. You see, most young women [5].................. .... go to university in those days. They [6].................. get married instead.

Tara: Could you choose your husband?

Rose: Oh yes! But women [7]..................................... have much freedom. Until 1918 women [8]............................... be able to vote in elections! And until 1928 they had to be thirty to vote.

Tara: Did your mother ever have a job?

Rose: She never earned any money but she [9].................. work very hard. She looked after her parents, her husband and her ten children.

Tara: When did she die?

Rose: In 1918. She was only fifty-two.

Tara: How sad!

Rose: Yes, it was very sad. I was only eighteen. In those days, people [10]................................. live so long. Perhaps it was because they [11]................................. have so many children.

Practice

● **Exclamations with** *so, such a/an*

5 Complete the sentences with *so, such* or *such a/an*.

I've never seen **such a** mess. Clean it up at once!

1 You are .... tall for thirteen. You look about eighteen!

2 It was a great holiday. We had .... brilliant time.

3 The film was extremely silly. I've never seen .... stupid film.

4 She's .... clever. She always gets the highest marks in the class.

5 He's really nice and he's got .... nice smile.

6 She always looks .... tired. I think she works very hard.

7 He's often very late. It's because he lives .... long way from the school.

8 Don't be .... annoying! Leave me alone.

9 They are .... nice people. They are always .... helpful and kind.

10 These are .... interesting photos. You must look at them.

11 Don't be .... lazy! Turn the TV off and come and play tennis.

● **Result clauses with** *so* **and** *such*

6 Match the sentence halves. Then join them with *so/such ... that*.

It was a funny book. `c`
The film was boring. `f`

1 It was a lovely day. ☐
2 The music was loud. ☐
3 It was delicious food. ☐
4 He's a liar. ☐
5 The sea was clear and blue. ☐
6 It was a wonderful moment. ☐
7 The sand was hot. ☐
8 The boat trips were cheap. ☐

a) I couldn't sleep.
b) I don't believe anything he says.
c) I fell off my chair laughing.
d) I'll never forget it.
e) They decided to go to the beach.
f) They fell asleep in the middle of it.
g) We couldn't stop eating it.
h) We had to dive in immediately.
i) We had to run across it.
j) We went on one every day.

It was such a funny book that I fell off my chair laughing.

The film was so boring that they fell asleep in the middle of it.

1 ....
....

2 ....
....

3 ....
....

4 ....
....

5 ....
....

6 ....
....

7 ....
....

8 ....
....

Unit 17

Grammar highlights

Reported statements

Direct speech

'He is French.'
'We're having fun.'
'I like chocolate.'
'They arrived on Tuesday.'
'I've found my purse.'
'We'll leave on Sunday.'
'I can't wait.'

Reported speech

He said (that) he was French.
They said (that) they were having fun.
She said (that) she liked chocolate.
I told her (that) they had arrived on Tuesday.
She said (that) she had found her purse.
They told me (that) they would leave on Sunday.
She told us (that) she couldn't wait.

● This chart shows the rules for tense changes after a past reporting verb such as *said* or *told*.

Direct speech	Reported speech
Present continuous →	Past continuous
Present simple →	Past simple
Past simple →	Past perfect
Present perfect →	Past perfect
can/will/may →	*could/would/ might*

● The word *that* can be omitted, e.g. *She said she hadn't had a good time.*

● *Tell* is always followed by an object pronoun or noun, e.g. *He told her he'd be late. He told Susie he'd be late.* If you use *say* and you want to mention who the speaker was talking to, you have to use *to*, e.g. *He said (to Susie) that he'd be late.*

● After a present tense reporting verb such as *say(s), tell(s)*, there are no tense changes, e.g. *'I'm hungry.' She says that she is hungry.*

Practice

● Reported statements

1 > Report what top US basketball star Michael Rivers said in a recent interview.

'The California Dolphins are a great team.'

1 'I was with the Boston Bears for three years.'

2 'My girlfriend doesn't often come to games.'

3 'She won't be at my next game.'

4 'She can't get the day off work!'

5 'My parents always come to watch.'

6 'They didn't want me to be a professional athlete.'

7 'Last year I earned $6,000,000.'

8 'I'll probably give up at the age of thirty.'

He said the California Dolphins were a great team.

1 ....

2 ....

3 ....

4 ....

5 ....

6 ....

7 ....

8 ....

● Reported speech

2 > Read the newspaper article. Write pop star Gina Devito's actual words to the reporter.

★★★★★★★★★★★★★★★★★★★★★★★★

Five minutes with

Gina

Gina Devito said that she didn't like interviews but she would speak to me for five minutes. [1] She said that I couldn't take any photos of her. [2] She added that her manager would give me a good photo if I needed one.

[3] She said she wouldn't answer any questions about her ex-boyfriend Mick Hankton. [4] She said rock and roll was the real love of her life. [5] She added that she loved all her fans.

[6] She told me that her band was going on tour in the USA in July. [7] She said they were all a bit nervous because they didn't like flying. [8] She said she had only been on a plane once.

★★★★★★★★★★★★★★★★★★★★★★★★

'I don't like interviews but I'll speak to you for five minutes.'

1 '..
....,

2 '..
....,

3 '..
....,

4 '..
....,

5 '..
....,

6 '..
....,

7 '..
....,

8 '..
....,

Practice

● **Reported statements**

3 ‣ Write what Rick and Julie said about their evening.

Rick

We had a lovely time.
1 I met Julie outside the cinema.
2 I was about ten minutes late.
3 She kindly paid for both of us.
4 The film had a very strange beginning.
5 We left early because it was so boring.
6 Julie is really interested in computers.
7 I'll definitely ask her out again.
8 I can't wait to see her again.

Julie

I didn't enjoy the evening.
1 I had to wait in the rain outside the cinema.
2 He was twenty minutes late.
3 He didn't bring any money.
4 We missed the beginning of the film so Rick didn't understand the story.
5 It was a brilliant film but Rick didn't want to stay to the end.
6 He talks about computers all the time.
7 I definitely won't go out with him again.
8 I can't remember a worse evening.

Rick said *they had had a lovely time*.

Julie said *she hadn't enjoyed the evening*.

1 Rick said ....

....

Julie said ....

....

2 Rick said ....

....

Julie said ....

....

3 Rick said ....

....

Julie said ....

....

4 Rick said ....

....

Julie said ....

....

5 Rick said ....

....

Julie said ....

....

6 Rick said ....

....

Julie said ....

....

7 Rick said ....

....

Julie said ....

....

8 Rick said ....

....

Julie said ....

....

Grammar highlights

Remember

Reported questions

Direct questions

Wh- **questions**

'What's your telephone number?'
'Where do you work?'
'When did you arrive?'
'Where have you left your bags?'

Yes/No **questions**

'Do you like your job?'
'Did you go to Sue's party?'
'Will you speak to Sam?'
'Can I get you a drink?'
'Have you bought a ticket?'

Reported questions

Wh- **questions**

He asked her what her telephone number was.
He asked her where she worked.
He asked her when she had arrived.
He asked her where she had left her bags.

Yes/No **questions**

He asked her if she liked her job.
He asked her if she had gone to Sue's party.
He asked her if she would speak to Sam.
He asked her if he could get her a drink.
He asked her if she had bought a ticket.

● The rules for tense changes in reported questions are the same as in reported statements.

● There are no tense changes after a reporting word in the present tense, e.g. *'What kind of music do you like?'* *I often ask people what kind of music they like.*

● In reported *Wh-* questions, we use the *Wh-* word + the subject + the verb. We do not use the interrogative form of the verb.

● In reported *Yes/No* questions, we use *if* + the subject + the verb. We do not use the interrogative form of the verb.

Practice

● Reported questions: *Wh-* questions

1 ⟩ Write who asked you each question. Then report the question.

How often do you clean your teeth?

(The dentist)

The dentist asked me how

often I cleaned my teeth.

1 Why haven't you tidied your room?

(.................................)

....

....

2 Why is your homework so untidy?

(.................................)

....

....

3 What time will you be back this evening?

(.................................)

....

....

4 How much did you pay for your jeans?

(.................................)

....

....

5 How long have you had this cough?

(.................................)

....

....

6 Why haven't you brought your atlas to the lesson?

(.................................)

....

....

7 What size trainers do you usually wear?

(.................................)

....

....

● Reported questions: *Yes/No* questions

2 ⟩ Decide which person in the box asked each prompt question. Then complete the reported questions.

- best friend ● brother ● taxi driver
- parents ● customs officer ● PE teacher
- shop assistant

Do you want to get out at the corner?

The **taxi driver** asked Jack **if he wanted to get**

out at the corner.

1 Is the blue jacket the right size?

The .... asked me ....

....

2 Did you buy any watches or cameras during your holiday?

The .... asked the man ....

....

3 Will you be free to play in the match on Saturday?

The .... asked Laura ....

....

4 Do you want a camera for your birthday?

Her .... asked her ....

....

5 Have you bought anything for Mum's birthday?

My .... asked me ....

....

6 Are you going to invite Sonia to the school disco?

Neil's .... asked him ....

....

Practice

● **Reported questions: mixed**

3 ＞ **Write the reported questions as direct questions in the correct places.**

a) He asked her how she knew that.

b) He asked her which dog she meant.

c) He asked her if it smelled good.

d) He asked her if she wanted to borrow his hat too.

e) He asked his sister if she could help him with his homework.

f) She asked her what it looked like.

g) She asked him if she could borrow his jacket.

h) She asked him if he was in love with a blonde girl called Cathy.

i) She asked him what he was making for supper.

j) She asked him what subject it was.

k) She asked the police officer if anyone had found her purse.

l) She asked the shop assistant how much the little dog was.

How much is the little dog?

Which dog do you mean?

139

Grammar highlights

Remember

too + **adjective/adverb** + *to*

She's too clever to make that mistake again.
She thinks too clearly to make that mistake.

(not) + **adjective/adverb** + *enough to*

He wasn't quick enough to catch the ball.
He didn't run quickly enough to catch the ball.
He's stupid enough to believe anything.

● *Too* goes before an adjective or adverb.
● *Enough* goes after an adjective or adverb.

Verb + **infinitive with** *to*

She offered to pay.
We agreed to do it.
They seemed to like the present.

These verbs take an infinitive with *to:*
decide, want, offer, promise, hope, agree, seem, manage, refuse, expect, learn, remember, forget, ask

Verb + **gerund (***-ing* **form)**

I don't mind helping.
They've finished cleaning the room.
We couldn't avoid seeing them.

These verbs take a gerund:
mind, enjoy, miss, finish, give up, avoid, practise, like, hate, love, stop

Practice

| • too + adjective/adverb + to |

1 ⟩ **Complete the sentences with** *too ... to* **and the correct word from the box.**

> • badly • busy • dangerous • young
> • dangerously • fast • exhausted • (heavy)
> • far away • short • tiny • slowly • late

The table was __*too heavy to*__ move.

1 Some things are .... see
without a microscope.

2 He ran .... win the race.

3 In my opinion, at eighteen you are ....
.... get married.

4 What did he say? I was standing ....
.... hear.

5 Those waves are huge. It's ....
.... swim here.

6 This music is .... dance to.

7 She's probably ....
be a model. I think you have to be 1 metre 70.

8 They stayed at home because it was ....
.... go to the cinema.

9 He was .... talk. He was cooking
a meal for fourteen people.

10 He was injured .... finish the
race.

11 He drives .... to pass his test.

12 I have to do the washing-up now. I was ....
.... do it last night.

| • (not) + adjective/adverb + enough to ... |

2 ⟩ **Read the article. Then write sentences about yourself with** *I'm (not) old enough to.*

Young people and the law

In Britain you can:

be arrested by the police at 10

1 buy a pet without your parents' permission at 12
2 get a part-time job at 13
3 work full time at 16
4 get married with your parents' permission at 16
5 join the army, if you're a boy, at 16
  join the army, if you're a girl, at 17
6 drive a car or motorbike at 17
7 vote at 18

Name: .... Age: ....

Male/Female: ....

In Britain:
I'm old enough to be arrested by the police.

1 ....
....
2 ....
....
3 ....
....
4 ....
....
5 ....
....
6 ....
....
7 ....
....

Practice

● *too ... to / not ... enough to*

3 ▷ **Complete the answers using** *too* **or** *not ... enough to* **with the word in brackets.**

Did he come by bike? (wet)
No, it was **too wet to come by bike.**

Do you want a pizza? (hungry)
No, thanks. I'm **not hungry enough to eat a pizza.**

1 Is she a good teacher? (impatient)
No, she's ....

....

2 Shall we go swimming? (warm)
No, it's ....

....

3 Did he buy her red roses? (romantic)
No, he's ....

....

4 Are you going to sing in the concert? (shy)
No, I'm ....

....

5 Did he shout at them? (polite)
No, he was ....

....

6 Can you get that box off the shelf? (tall)
Sorry, I'm ....

....

● *too ... to / n't (not) ... enough to*

4 ▷ **Complete the letter using** *too ... to* **or** *n't ... enough to* **with an adjective from the box.**

> ● calm ● (cold) ● crowded ● expensive
> ● far ● nervous ● old ● small ● sociable
> ● strong ● windy

Camp Sun

Beach Road,
Eastsea,
ES1 6ID
Tel: 012665 985674

20th July

Dear Sam,

I'm having an awful time at Camp Sun. Firstly, the sea is far __too cold to__ swim in unless you have a wetsuit. And the swimming pool here at Camp Sun is [1]........................... have a real swim. It's only about 3 metres long! James and I lay on the beach yesterday but there were lots of clouds and the sun was [2]........................... give us a tan. We couldn't read our newspapers because it was [3]........................... hold them and we both got sand in our eyes!

The jet-skis are [4]........................... rent and the sea is [5]........................... learn to sail. We're both [6]........................... try parascending. So we aren't doing much! We are [7]........................... rent motorbikes (we're only 16 and you have to be 17) and Camp Sun is 15 miles from the nearest village so it's [8]........................... walk to it.

The Camp Sun café is OK but it's often [9]........................... get a seat there. We went to the camp disco a few days ago but the girls were [10]........................... talk or dance with us.

Sorry about this boring letter. Things can only get better, I suppose!

Best wishes,
Mark

Practice

● too ... to / not ... enough to

5 ﹥ **Make two sentences into one sentence using** *too ... to* **or** *not enough to.*

She was driving very fast; she couldn't stop in time.

She was driving too fast to stop in time.

He wasn't driving very slowly; he didn't see the name of the street.

He wasn't driving slowly enough to see the name of the street.

1 He drives very aggressively; he isn't a good driver.

....

....

2 He didn't jump very high; he didn't break the record.

....

....

3 They all got up very late; they couldn't catch the early bus.

....

....

4 I couldn't see very clearly; I couldn't read the time on the clock.

....

....

5 We didn't wake up very early; we didn't see the sunrise.

....

....

6 He types very slowly; he can't get a job as a secretary.

....

....

● Verb followed by infinitive or gerund

6 ﹥ **Complete the sentences, putting the verbs into the correct form: infinitive or gerund.**

I don't enjoy __swimming__ (swim) in cold water.

She didn't want __to upset__ (upset) him so she told a white lie.

1 Anita has given up .... (eat) sweets and chocolate.

2 When did David decide .... (join) a circus?

3 I don't mind .... (look after) your little brother this evening.

4 Why has nobody offered .... (clean) the kitchen floor?

5 If we go away this weekend, we'll miss .... (see) Angela and Tony.

6 She promised .... (write) to me every day but she hasn't.

7 I expected .... (be) terrified on my first parachute jump, but I wasn't.

8 He needs to practise .... (park) before his driving test on Monday.

9 How did you avoid .... (get) wet in the storm this morning?

10 Meg always seems .... (have) much more money than everyone else.

11 Eric refused .... (wear) a suit and tie to the dinner party.

12 They haven't finished .... (discuss) the football match.

13 How did you manage .... (mend) your bike?

14 They haven't yet agreed .... (pay) for the broken window.

15 I hope .... (see) you again soon.

Irregular verbs

Infinitive	Past simple	Past participle
be	was	been
beat	beat	beaten
become	became	become
begin	began	begun
bite	bit	bitten
blow	blew	blown
break	broke	broken
bring	brought	brought
build	built	built
burn	burnt/burned	burnt/burned
buy	bought	bought
catch	caught	caught
choose	chose	chosen
come	came	come
cost	cost	cost
cut	cut	cut
do	did	done
draw	drew	drawn
dream	dreamt/dreamed	dreamt/dreamed
drink	drank	drunk
drive	drove	driven
eat	ate	eaten
fall	fell	fallen
feed	fed	fed
feel	felt	felt
fight	fought	fought
find	found	found
fly	flew	flown
forget	forgot	forgotten
freeze	froze	frozen
get	got	got
give	gave	given
go	went	gone
grow	grew	grown
have	had	had
hear	heard	heard
hide	hid	hidden
hit	hit	hit
hold	held	held
hurt	hurt	hurt
keep	kept	kept
know	knew	known
lay	laid	laid
lead	led	led
leap	leapt	leapt
learn	learnt/learned	learnt/learned
leave	left	left
lend	lent	lent
let	let	let
lie	lay	lain

Infinitive	Past simple	Past participle
lose	lost	lost
make	made	made
mean	meant	meant
meet	met	met
pay	paid	paid
put	put	put
read	read	read
ride	rode	ridden
ring	rang	rung
rise	rose	risen
run	ran	run
say	said	said
see	saw	seen
sell	sold	sold
send	sent	sent
set	set	set
shake	shook	shaken
shine	shone	shone
shoot	shot	shot
show	showed	shown/showed
shrink	shrank/shrunk	shrunk
shut	shut	shut
sing	sang	sung
sink	sank	sunk
sit	sat	sat
sleep	slept	slept
smell	smelt	smelt
speak	spoke	spoken
spend	spent	spent
spill	spilt	spilt
split (up)	split (up)	split (up)
spread	spread	spread
stand	stood	stood
steal	stole	stolen
strike	struck	struck
sweep	swept	swept
swim	swam	swum
swing	swung	swung
take	took	taken
teach	taught	taught
tear	tore	torn
tell	told	told
think	thought	thought
throw	threw	thrown
understand	understood	understood
wake (up)	woke (up)	woken (up)
wear	wore	worn
weep	wept	wept
win	won	won
write	wrote	written